Our Debt to Greece and Rome

EDITORS

GEORGE DEPUE HADZSITS, PH.D.

DAVID MOORE ROBINSON, PH.D., LL.D.

GREEK BIOLOGY
AND MEDICINE

BY
HENRY OSBORN TAYLOR

COOPER SQUARE PUBLISHERS, INC.
NEW YORK
1963

Published 1963 by Cooper Square Publishers, Inc.
59 Fourth Avenue, New York 3, N. Y.
Library of Congress Catalog Card No. 63-10282

EDITORS' PREFACE

MANY READERS will find in the pages of Doctor Taylor a revelation in the amazing advance made by Greek Biology and Medicine and in the extent of our indebtedness to Hippocrates, Aristotle and Galen. The subject is one not so well known as some other aspects of the Greek and Roman civilizations. We are apt to think of magic and superstition in the medical practice of the ancients, in spite of our Celsus and the oracular Pliny. The specialist may have followed the expositions of Sir William Osler, Dr. Charles Singer, Sir Clifford Allbutt and Dr. Arthur J. Brock, but this book is addressed to the layman. It is our hope that a wider and deeper interest will result in the achievements of those Greeks who laid the foundations, permanent and secure, for the sciences of Biology and Medicine.

The history of the *influence* of the Greek biologists and medical men still remains to be written, but it will be a fascinating chapter in the history of human culture. When the time arrives, we shall have a record of fanatic devotion, of literal and uninspired acceptance, of forgetfulness, of an inspiring rediscovery with a quickening of scientific interest, of direct observation of Nature's phenomena, with a consequent skepticism toward ancient dogma, and of a final great scientific revival which has resulted in a recognition of the true worth of the ancients. Through the mazes of Arabic civilization, over the collapse of the religious medieval period and the pride of the Renaissance, through the fourteenth and sixteenth centuries, the great ancients have come to us. It is largely through their inspiration that we have learned our independent pursuit of Nature's mysteries in the courageous *Greek* spirit of love of truth, reason and freedom. Doubtless in the field of medicine, this has carried with it a certain emancipation, as Gilbert Murray has said, from the dead hand of the past, but it is an emancipation from the errors of the past alone. The twentieth century is gradually approaching a true appraisal of the values of the ancient medicine and biology, so eloquently expressed years ago in Darwin's gracious phrase.

Dr. Taylor's volume on " Greek Biology and Medicine " is the third to appear in the new Library, " Our Debt to Greece and Rome." The author has drawn his sketch in such a way as to make clear the influence of ancient biological and medical theories and of the ancient medical practice upon our intellectual life, to-day, giving frequent allusions to that influence as it affected distinguished biologists and men of medicine during the intervening centuries. This is part of the larger plan of the Library as a whole to show in some detail the vitality of the ancient thought and to make more articulate the significance it possesses for us. We all too unconsciously accept a heritage — scientific, intellectual, spiritual — which lies at the very core of our being and is the real hope of an orderly future.

This book takes no formal account of the famous Pompeian medical instruments, and only further study of the Ebers papyrus and in particular of the Edwin Smith papyrus may lead to a new estimate of the progress of medicine in ancient Egypt; but we are not yet in a position to estimate the truth contained in these venerable documents. And, for us, Greece still stands as the pioneer in a science which will progress to its greatest victories as it is quickened with the nobility of spirit that touched the heart and mind of Hippocrates. His words find an eloquent echo in the lines of Goethe:

Ach Gott! die Kunst ist lang
Und kurz ist unser Leben,

which are an immortal commentary on the inner essence of the Greek's aspiration.

CONTENTS

[xi]

PREFACE

THE OBJECT of this little monograph is to indicate the debt of the modern world to the ancient biology and medicine. One might as well say simply *Greek* biology and medicine, since whether pursued or practiced in Ionia, in Attica, or in Rome, the biology and medicine worthy of our attention were Greek in their origin and progress, and owed little to the Romans. The scientific spirit was an endowment of Hellas, and alien from the genius of Rome; nor did the Romans capture much of it from the gifted race whom they subdued politically, and by whose art and literature they were captivated in turn.

The task before us might make the labor of a lifetime for any writer, and the resulting volume would inevitably lead the reader into long winding avenues. I offer but a sketch, a slight sketch as it were, of Greek biology and medicine. I have endeavored to draw it in such a way as to make clear the nature of their influence upon our intellectual life today. So we gain a useful point of view from which to consider the pregnant thoughts and researches of the Greeks regarding the nature of animals and plants, and their wise practice of the healing art. We may profit by the spirit in which they made their investigations and applied a system of therapeutics, scientifically based.

Our correlated modern sciences which are called biological because they treat of living organisms, have pushed their researches and discoveries far beyond the achievements of the Greeks. They are not a graft upon a Greek stem: they have arisen through the direct study of nature, not from the old Greek books. Thus they have shown a Greek spirit. It is in this modern renewal of a scientific mind, rather than in any specific borrowings from the ancient stock, that we should seek to recognize what Greece has been and still may be for us.

So with medicine. The reign of Galen ended some centuries ago. But modern medicine, in spite of its vastly increased knowledge, has never ceased to hark back, and often very consciously, to the principles of Hippocrates. With a larger knowledge than his own, it rightly reverences the great Greek, and treads still in his footsteps. Therefore in considering our debt to Greek medicine I shall look to the Hippocratic *method,* rather than to specific points of practice, referring to these more by way of illustration.

I have to thank my friend, Dr. Frederic S. Lee, Research Professor of Physiology in Columbia University, for his valuable suggestions upon reading my manuscript; also the New York Academy of Medicine for the privileges of its great medical library courteously extended. My friend, Professor Heidel of Wesleyan University has aided me throughout my work with books and counsel, and has had the kindness to read my proof and advise with me regarding it. His eminence in the field of Hippocratic studies and early Greek philosophy is known to all scholars. The italics in the text are due to Professor Hadzsits, one of the Editors in this series, who is also responsible for the " Outline, briefly showing the influence of Greek Biology and Medicine," printed as an Appendix to this volume.

HENRY OSBORN TAYLOR

NEW YORK,
October, 1922.

GREEK BIOLOGY AND MEDICINE

GREEK BIOLOGY AND MEDICINE

I. THE EARLY BIOLOGY

BEYOND all other ancient people, the better sort of men among the dwellers in the Ionian cities on the west coast of Asia Minor and the neighboring islands were blessed with lively intellectual curiosity. They were also free, and meant to keep their freedom. Their cities might for a time be brought within the sway of a Lydian monarch or the Great King of Persia; but such intermittent pressure from without did not hamper the commerce of these coast and island towns, or restrict the free thinking of their citizens. Religion was tolerant or uncertain; there was no constraining caste of priests. Men might think as they saw fit upon the origin and order of the world, and freely express their opinions. And it came to pass that the gifted thought-leaders of Ionian Greece devised conceptions of

[3]

the world, the impress of which has never been expunged from human thinking.

The old Ionian speculation upon Nature or φύσις was curious as to the material of the world, and considered how its visible component rocks and earth and waters came to be. This speculation, supplemented by investigation, was directed also to the origins of plants and animals, to the manner of their growth and to their living structure. Accordingly, the φυσιολογία, which is to say the natural history or philosophy, of these physicists, included the beginnings of biology, which is the science of all living things, if we use this comparatively modern word in its most comprehensive sense.

There is no need to re-state the physical theories of the early Ionian philosophers and of their compeers who were Greeks even when not so evidently Ionians. It is more to our purpose to remark that for us Greek biology begins in some extraordinary fragments ascribed to the great Milesian Anaximander, who was a younger friend of Thales and lived through the first half of the sixth century before Christ. They are as follows:

" Living creatures arose from the moist element as it was evaporated by the sun. Man was like another animal, namely, a fish, in the beginning.

" The first animals were produced in the moisture, each enclosed in a prickly bark. As they advanced in age, they came out upon the drier part. When the bark broke off, they survived for a short time.

" Further, he says that originally man was born from animals of another species. His reason is that while other animals quickly find food by themselves, man alone requires a lengthy period of suckling. Hence, had he been originally as he is now, he would never have survived.

" He declares that at first human beings arose in the inside of fishes, and after having been reared like sharks, and become capable of protecting themselves, they were finally cast ashore and took to land." [1]

We may puzzle ourselves and find much or little in these syncopated fragments. They do not disclose the manner of Anaximander's investigations, but represent his conclusions, which were drawn from his study of nature. They stand for his explanations of the visible facts, his accounting for phenomena. This dawning biology, like the cosmological physics of which it appears as part, was free from superstitious fear; it admitted no magic, recognized no supernatural; it had little religious awe. Such unembarrassed observation of nature, such free and rational conclusions, were unique in the world; and unique the consequent endeavor to build up a systematic body of natural knowledge, with accordant hypotheses, or explanations, which should rationally account for the world in which man lived. Even with the Greeks these intellectual aims were not to become common. And as such an observation of nature was then utterly unknown in Babylonia or Egypt or anywhere else on earth, so outside of the elect of the Greek race and a very few others who imbibed their spirit, it was never accepted by the ancient world.

And here at once be it said that, taking full account of the admirable Greek achievements in biology and medicine, our modern indebtedness is less for their substance than for the clear spirit of scientific investigation which was one of the immortal legacies of Greece, however few the men or periods that could accept it. In medicine, in surgery, in every field of science, modern investigation has advanced very far beyond the Greeks. It has not, however, altogether improved upon their spirit, although in practice it has brought the habit of careful and toilsome verification which was not theirs. Yet the *methods* of modern medicine have ever and anon been fain to hark back to the broad wisdom of Hippocrates; and as for the genius and accomplishment of Aristotle in biology, why, he will reappear as Harvey's god and Darwin's admiration.[2]

After Anaximander, other natural philosophers thought much upon the origin of plants and animals. Biological considerations and medical doctrines appear in the fragments of the early philosophers and fill out the traditions of their lives, — with Anaxagoras, in his recognition of the differences between living organisms and inanimate objects, with Empedocles, presumably an important figure in the history of medicine, with Democritus, a dissector and penetrating investigator, of whom Aristotle said that no one had so profoundly considered growth and change.

Can we discover a general purpose in their investigations and reflections? Possibly, — by a moderate use of constructive interpretation. They were searching for the source and cause

of living things: pondering upon the first in-
choate material of them, and the moving
influences of warmth and moisture; then considering the reasons and manner of their growth
and sustenance, noting the features of their
structure. In the Homeric Epics, the fortunes
and fatalities of men and beasts were frequently determined by the arbitrary will and
action of the gods. Such a pantheon could
have no place in the minds of men searching
for a plastic source and for operative causes
which should be constant and regular, depend-
able and even predictable, in their action.
With these men " the conception of Nature
replaced that of the gods as a basis of explanation, φύσις was conceived as the source of the
manifold activities of the world." [3]

These early philosophers, Pre-Socratics, as
they are called, had not analyzed causation
or distinguished one manner of cause from
another. That was left for Aristotle. They
had no distinct conception of final causes or
the purposeful adaptation of means to ends.
" Lucky for them! " many of us moderns
might remark. Nevertheless, to them, Nature,
the source of things if one will, seemed to contain the moving principles which issued in the

[8]

world of plants and animals, and ruled within or over them. These initial and controlling forces might be conceived as utterly mechanical, as in the later Atomic theory of Democritus. Yet some of the early Greeks, observing the obvious conformity of means to ends, at least in animals, could not rest in the thought of Nature as merely mechanical and without purpose in its operation. Besides, plants and animals were alive, and life could not really be explained in terms of weight and impetus. Since Nature was the source and fashioner of living beings, Nature itself, or *herself*, might in the end be thought of as alive. The concrete, vital, form-and-life-giving character of Greek thinking could hardly keep from vitalizing its concept of the great source and mother of living things. Heraclitus had already said that " Nature loves to hide," or " play at hide-and-seek." When has she not been found the cleverest of players at this game?

So the early and the later Greeks touched delicately on the living vitality and possibly vague personality of Nature. If divine, Nature was pantheistically so, and never to be moulded to the sharp personality of an Homeric Zeus or Apollo or Athena.

There exist but fragments of the Pre-Socratics, and Xenophon's *Memoirs* of Socrates
contain scant notice of biology or physics.
Recently it has been recognized that a mine
of suggestion, if not information, as to the
early Greek thoughts upon the working of
Nature in living organisms is to be found in
that large and most significant body of medical and even biological literature which trails
the authorship of Hippocrates. He was Socrates' contemporary; and although it is difficult to prove his authorship of any one of these
treatises, a goodly part are from the fifth
century, when he lived, and are convincingly
associated with the great physician to whom
they are ascribed. Other portions of the
Hippocratic *corpus* are affected by the theories
of the natural philosophers, and reflect contemporary conceptions of Nature.

For example: " Hippocrates speaks of
Nature as arranging the vitals in the inner
parts; says of the auricles of the heart that
they are instruments by which she takes in the
air, adding that they seem to be the handiwork
of a good craftsman; refers to the *vis medicatrix naturae,* Nature having discovered the
methods without understanding and untaught;

she makes glands and hair; she (as the student's natural aptitude or inaptitude) can prepare the way for and offer resistance to instruction; she is all-sufficient; she produces natural species and legislates language; in disease she may withhold signs, but may be constrained by art to yield them; the means employed by her are likened to the means in use in the arts." [4]

One of the Hippocratic treatises, probably dating from the close of the fifth century, gives much zoölogical information, and even suggests something like a classification of animals and plants. Another, somewhat later in date, discusses with great intelligence the generation of animals and plants. It is a worthy predecessor of Aristotle's works upon these matters. [5]

II. THE HIPPOCRATICS

GREEK MEDICINE, with surgery, was an art, the healing art, *ἰα ρικὴ τέχνη*. Through its ministrations men and women, the highest order of living beings, were healed of their wounds or, when sick, restored to health. Such was medicine in its broad Hippocratic foundations, which consciously rested upon still more ancient medical experience. But since the doctors were thinking men and also Greeks, they sought to know the causes of sickness; some of them speculated on the nature of man and invented hypotheses of disease. So medicine inclined to theory, besides relying on the results of observation of the sick; it tended to become a science as well as an art. Members of the healing craft studied anatomy and physiology (in the modern sense), which are biological sciences. Indeed so far as medicine became science as well as art, it falls within the province of biology.

Greek medicine and natural philosophy or

science were to progress and retrograde together. I refer to the true Greek medical
tradition; for there were quacks in Greece,
as there have been ever since; today people
still troop after them. But in speaking of our
debt to Greece in medicine, we have in mind
the broad currents of good practice and increasing knowledge which flow full in the Hippocratic writings, continue on through the great
physicians and anatomists of Alexandria, and
spread themselves abroad over the Roman
Empire until, six hundred years after Hippocrates, they are brought together in the ample
system of Galen. It is convenient to proceed
chronologically in this little attempt to follow
the interrelations of Greek biology and
medicine.

The almost consciously schematic and introductory tract *On Ancient Medicine* is
usually placed first in the Hippocratic writings.[6]
As its name implies, and its contents make
clear, it sets forth no novel system, but bases
its argument upon the experience and clinical
observation of generations. Like other writings
of the master, or his immediate school, it will
steer a safe course between a crude and haphazard empiricism and distorting the teach-

ings of rationalized experience into agreement with hypotheses touching the nature and diseases of man or the things of heaven and **earth.**

Thus the tract opens: " There are those who have essayed to speak or write concerning medicine, basing their argument on the hot or cold, on the moist or the dry or anything else they choose, reducing the causes of human diseases and death to a minimum, one and the same for all, basing their argument on one or two [such causes]; but in many of the novelties they utter they are clearly in the wrong. This is the more blameworthy, because they err touching an actual art which all men employ in the greatest emergencies and in which they honor most the skillful practitioners. Now there are practitioners, some bad, some excellent; which would not be true if medicine were not actually an art, and no observations or discoveries had been made in it. All would be equally unskilled and ignorant of it, and the cure of diseases would be wholly subject to chance. As a matter of fact, it is not so; but, as artisans in all other arts excel one the other in handicraft and knowledge, so also in medicine.[7] Therefore I maintained that it had no need of vain hypotheses, as is the case in matters inaccessible to sense and open to doubt. Concerning these, if one essay to speak, one must resort to hypothesis. So, if one should speak and entertain an opinion touching things in the heavens or under the earth, it would be clear neither to the speaker nor to those who heard him whether his opinion was true or false; for there is no appeal to aught that can establish the truth." [8]

The tract proceeds to show that the art of medicine has grown through observation of the needs and diseases of men, — not through the acceptance of some hypothesis as to their cause.[9] For example, the regulation of the patient's diet, especially in acute illness, was fundamental in Hippocratic medicine. And the tract argues that no improvement in diet, even for people in health, could have come about except through observation of the ill effects of unsuitable food. Much more, then, has long clinical experience shown the need to modify the regimen of a patient suffering from a fever. Indeed nothing has so promoted the art of medicine as observing how the food for a healthy man injures the sick, and the consequent endeavor to regulate the patient's regimen and discover the form and amount of nourishment suitable to a constitution weakened through disease.

The obvious fact that some forms of food will make a well person sick tells against those who imagine that disease is produced by an excess of warmth or cold, of dryness or moisture. " For if hot, or cold, or moist, or dry, be that which proves injurious to man, and if the person who would treat him properly must apply cold to the hot, hot to the cold, moist to the dry, and dry to the moist — then let a man eat wheat raw from the threshing floor, and raw meat, and drink water with it.[10] By using such a diet I know that he will suffer severely; for he will experience pains, his body will become weak and his bowels deranged, and he will not live long. What remedy then should be provided him? Hot, or cold? or moist? or dry? For, according to the hypothesis, it must be one of these that is injuring the patient, and must be removed by its contrary. But the surest and most obvious way is to change his diet, give bread instead of wheat, boiled flesh in the place of raw, and a little wine." [11]

Having ridiculed and disproved such hypotheses in their application to medicine, the

writer passes on to question the usefulness of
other philosophic theories for the medical practitioner: " Certain physicians and philosophers
assert that one cannot know medicine without
knowing what man is, how he originally came
into existence and of what substances he was
compounded in the beginning. . . . Now the
contention of these men really looks to philosophy, as do Empedocles and others who
have written concerning nature (περὶ Φύσεως).
As for me, I consider that what a philosopher
or physician has said or written of Nature has
less relevancy to medicine than to painting;
and I am of opinion that, so far as concerns
knowledge of Nature, one can know nothing
definite about it except from medicine; but
this may be thoroughly learned, when men go
about it rightly. Hitherto, it seems to me, we
are far from it: far, that is to say, from having
a scientific knowledge of what man is (that
is to say, what his constitution is) and to what
cause he owes his origin and the rest, in any
exact sense. Now so much at least it is indis-
pensable that the physician should know concerning Nature and should greatly concern
himself to know, if he is to do any part of his
duty; to wit, what a man is (i.e. what his

constitution is), relative to meat and drink, and what he is relative to the rest of his mode of life, and what results follow for the individual from particular things, and all this not merely in general terms, as e.g., ' cheese is unwholesome food, for it distresses one who eats plentifully of it '; but what particular distress it causes, and for what reason, and to what ingredient of the man's constitution it is unsuitable." [12]

The writer points to the physician's need to consider this question closely. Each individual is peculiarly constituted, and cheese will be injurious or strengthening as it may or may not suit his constitution. Here the writer tacitly accepts the Hippocratic conception of the four humors representing the four elemental qualities of every human body: the blood contains the warm-moist quality; yellow bile, the warm-dry; black bile, the cold-dry; and phlegm (formed in the brain), the cold-moist. Although these humors do not exist in the same proportions in every individual, nevertheless each person's health depends upon their due relations and blending, while an abnormal preponderance or accumulation of any one of them produces disease. Though the disturbance display itself only in one spot, general symptoms of illness will follow. It is food that furnishes the material from which these humors, or cardinal fluids, renew themselves.

This conception of the humors and the effects of their disturbance was the chief pillar of the medical temple for the next two thousand years, and became part of the current speech of European peoples. Although not universally accepted in Greek medicine, it received the authoritative approval of Galen and then of Avicenna, the Arabian physician and philosopher of the eleventh century; and no one stood out against them until the prodigious Paracelsus, than whom no man was ever more vociferously dubbed quack and charlatan by his own as well as later times.

Strictly taken, the theory of the four humors was as baseless as Paracelsus said it was; yet the conception of functional coördination among the human organs and of the general disturbance resulting from the sickness of any one of them, has never been discarded. Hippocrates viewed the body as a whole and had observed that the sickness of a part might disorder or sicken the rest. This might be understood by means of the four humors, which seemed to Hippocrates the nearest explanation of the observed phenomena.

Thus a certain amount of hypothesis entered the Hippocratic healing art; — as it necessarily makes part of every art as well as every science. But Hippocrates at least economized in hypothesis as few men after him, and very consciously. For he was an acute Ionian Greek, and the need to seek and formulate explanations, that is, hypotheses, comes with great urgency to every intelligent and inquiring mind. Babylonians and Egyptians, who were practical, but not intellectually curious, were not beset with any like cravings. And indeed the history of Greek, as well as modern, medicine will illustrate this competitive endeavor of the intellectual mind to keep its explanations abreast of observation; — indeed explanations, hypotheses, in the endeavor to keep abreast, to account for phenomena, *save the appearances* (σώζειν τὰ φαινόμενα, a Platonic phrase), will constantly go beyond them, and so astray. All progressive physical science, and medicine striving ever to become a science, exhibit this struggle of hypothesis to account for observation. And doubtless the more modest working hypotheses, which the true scientist or the good physician holds himself in readiness to abandon, are the most serviceable and least fatal.

We return to our illustrations of Hippocrates. Very typical is the treatment of the patient's regimen. Its method and humane wisdom are shown in the tract *On Regimen in Acute Diseases*. It opens somewhat warmly in a polemic against the Cnidian school for their fine-spun diagnoses and meticulous distinctions between diseases, which went beyond their knowledge of the course and nature of disease and far beyond their too restricted remedies. Not every variation of symptom means a different disease; and the Cnidians fail to consider those profounder indications of which the patient is not aware, but the physician must discern and understand if he would foresee the course and crisis of the sickness with which he must cope. Diet is most important in acute diseases, and has not been sufficiently determined; its effect upon the sick must be carefully considered and compared. The tract proceeds to do this specifically and most wisely; comparing, for instance, the results obtained from a diet of barley broth with those from strained barley water, and discussing whether the patient should have been previously purged. Attention is to be paid to the stages of the disease and the condition of the patient, and regard should be had to his usual habit of taking food, whether once a day or twice (*sic*). The physician must be cautious in changing the diet or increasing it when the disease takes a favorable turn. Greek physicians had constantly to treat pleurisies and pneumonias and enteric fevers; and one may question whether modern medical writing has anything wiser to say as to diet in such cases than this Hippocratic tract.

It is not my purpose to recount the details of Hippocratic practice, but rather to illustrate its principles, its penetrating observation, its fine and broad intelligence, its humane wisdom. Never was a practice so wise within the limitations of the practitioner's knowledge: that indeed was very limited as to anatomy and physiology, — while the resources of the human constitution were better understood, as were the effects of climate and food.

Hippocratic medicine recognized that diseases resulted from *natural* causes, and should be treated accordingly. This was a prodigious stride toward the light. It is always the task of medicine to trace the true causes, as well as the probable course, of a disease; and so learn to prevent or, if not that, to control and cure. Outside of Greece, as in Egypt or Babylonia, physicians could not cease to be priests or astrologers. There was surgery and some medicine practiced in those lands; but the practice could not quite disregard supposed demoniacal causes of disease or detach itself from the panacea of magic. These superstitions were stumbling blocks before the advance of medicine as a science or an art, progressing through knowledge and skill drawn from observation and experience. Their complete elimination first comes before us in the Hippocratic writings. It was part of the Greek freeing of the human spirit from foolish anxieties and irrelevant considerations; a putting things in their right places, — their right categories, human and divine, natural and supernatural, if the latter existed at all. Indeed the superhuman and divine might be just the other side, another aspect of the human and material, — just as much part of the universal order and just as subject to law.

The classic Hippocratic argument for this principle is in the tract *On the Sacred Disease,* epilepsy, which commonly was regarded as a stroke or visitation of a god or demon. But, says the writer, " it appears to me to be nowise more divine nor more sacred than other diseases, but has a natural cause from which it originates like other affections. Men regard its nature and cause as divine from ignorance and wonder, because it is not at all like to other diseases. And this notion of its divinity is kept up by their inability to comprehend it, and the simplicity of the mode by which it is treated, for men are freed from it by purifications and incantations. But if it is reckoned divine because it is wonderful, instead of one there are many diseases which would be sacred; for, as I will show, there are others no less wonderful and prodigious, which nobody imagines to be sacred. The quotidian, tertian and quartan fevers seem to me no less sacred and divine in their origin than this disease, though they are not reckoned so wonderful. And I see men become mad and demented from no manifest cause. . . . They who first referred this disease [epilepsy] to the gods, appear to me to have been just such persons as the conjurers, purificators, mountebanks, and charlatans now are, who give themselves out for being excessively religious, and as knowing more than other people. Such persons, then, using the divinity as a pretext and screen of their own inability to afford any assistance, have given out that the disease is sacred, adding suitable reasons for this opinion; they have instituted a mode of treatment which is safe for themselves, namely by applying purifications and incantations, and enforcing abstinence from baths and many articles of food which are unwholesome to sick men. . . ." [13]

After a statement of the causes of the disease within the human body or arising from outer influences, the conclusion follows, that " this disease called sacred comes from the same causes as the others, from cold, from the sun, or from changing winds. These are divine; but they do not make this disease more divine than others. All are human and divine and each has its own nature and power."

So each disease has its own nature and cannot arise without natural causes, — a beautiful and enlightened view for which we have so largely to thank Hippocrates.

The principle that disease and health are due to natural causes is exemplified in the large by the Hippocratic tract *On Airs, Waters and*

Places, which also illustrates the broad Hippocratic view of the province of medicine. It is the earliest essay known on the influence of physical environment upon health, disease and temperament. It holds that the intelligent physician must understand the effects of the situation or exposure of a city, of the varying seasons and the different winds, the quality of the water, the nature of the soil, and the inhabitants. It treats of climate and the diseases which prevail in certain localities from their exposure to certain winds; of the kinds of water and their effect upon the human body, for example in the formation of urinary *calculi.* The influence of the season is then set forth; and finally the effect of climate and despotic institutions in inducing the mild and unwarlike dispositions of the peoples of Asia, whose spirit is enslaved; while the mountainous and well-watered lands of Europe, with their sharp changes of season, have produced enterprising and warlike, or even ferocious inhabitants.

Such is a scanty outline of this penetrating presentation of matters which have been under the sharpest discussion, and from so many points of view, in the last hundred years. Without agreeing with all the statements of this great opening treatise, one will not fail to admire its profound intelligence.

So Hippocrates saw the natural causes of disease in such matters as unsuitable food or evil indulgence, unhealthy occupations, climate and the changing seasons. He had also observed the effect of heredity and the strength of individual constitutions on their proneness to disease. The office of medicine, of all medical treatment, was to assist the natural recuperative powers of the patient to throw off the disease. This Hippocratic idea of nature's *vis medicatrix* was hardly an hypothesis, so open to observation was the tendency of wounds to heal and of sick people to recover.

For treatment Hippocrates relied upon the clinical observation of the course of acute disease and the significance of pathological symptoms, recognized from the contrast exhibited with the state of the body in health. Symptoms had always local significance; usually they indicated further physical disturbance. Let a comprehensive and whole view be taken of the case, with careful consideration of every indication of the patient's condition and chances of recovery. The symptoms were considered generally as the phenomena of acute

[27]

disease.[14] Viewed in this way they were more knowable, their significance better understood, than the finer distinctions between one disease and another which admittedly outran the knowledge of these practitioners. In practice this generic knowledge was carefully adapted to the particular case. The patient himself was studied, his peculiar constitution taken account of, and his symptoms were treated with reference to his condition. These physicians were not tabulating diseases, they were set upon meeting the exigencies of each case — trying " to do good to the patient, or at least not harm him."

Accordingly, instead of finely distinguishing diagnoses of the different diseases, Hippocrates and his school worked out a general prognosis, a detailed and comprehensive exposition of the symptoms and course of acute disease, as exemplified in pleurisy or pneumonia, and in those various fevers so common in Greece. This is the theme of the προγνωστικόν or *Prognosis*, one of the most authentic of the Hippocratic writings: " He seems to me the best physician who is able to know in advance " the entire group of phenomena constituting the disease, to wit, to divine its previous conduct, its present action, its future course. Thus he will be able to supplement the patient's faulty statements, gain his confidence, keep clear of blame and be the better able to manage a cure when that is possible.

In order that the physician may have such knowledge, the *Prognosis* gives a close description of phenomena common to acute diseases: describes the look of the countenance, the patient's position in bed, the movements of his hands, the respiration, sweats, the dropsies which supervene, the sleep, the urine, faeces, vomitings and sputa, — contrasting these phenomena with those of the body in a state of health. That his countenance be like that of a person in health is the best of symptoms, while the worst is that it should show a contrast in every respect; to wit: "a sharp nose, hollow eyes, collapsed temples; the ears cold, contracted, and their lobes turned out; the skin about the forehead being rough, distended and parched; the color of the whole face being green, black, livid, or lead colored." [15] Unless such a face can be at once accounted for by some special reason, like want of food or sleep, the patient will surely die.

This is the famous *facies Hippocratica*, the

[29]

most frequently translated and imitated description of a face of a dying man: " for his nose was as sharp as a pen," says the Hostess of the dying Falstaff.

Space fails me for the writer's description of unfavorable signs from the patient's position in bed, — as " lying upon his back, with hands, neck, and legs extended," or his wishing to sit erect at the climax of the disease, especially in pneumonia, or waving his hands before his face, or hunting as if gathering bits of straw or picking the nap from the coverlet: " for after I saw him fumble with the sheets, and play with flowers, and smile upon his fingers' ends, I knew there was but one way," still says the Hostess, who had not read Hippocrates, but doubtless had seen old men die before.

There is scarcely a statement in this writing that has failed to leave its impress upon medicine: witness, for example, the cult which has surrounded its statement of the periodic crises in acute disease. The writing closes substantially with these words: " He who would know correctly beforehand those that will recover, and those that will die, and in what cases the disease will be protracted or shortened, must be able to judge from a thorough acquaintance with all the symptoms and a comparison of their weightiness, not omitting a consideration of the season of the year, yet being sure that at every season bad symptoms prognosticate ill and favorable symptoms good. . . . You should not complain because the name of any disease may not be mentioned here, for you may know all such as come to a crisis in the above mentioned times by the same symptoms."

The *Prognosis* reflects the spirit and the method of Hippocrates. Its refusal to follow diagnoses into distinctions between diseases which lay beyond any physician's knowledge was part of this method and spirit; likewise its decision to abide by clinical experience of acute disease and the significance of constantly occurring symptoms. This safer knowledge enabled the physician to foresee the course of his patient's sickness, and if possible conduct it to a cure. The salutary conception of a sickness as a chain of phenomena, as a whole, with a past, a present and a future, would keep the physician's healing art from crude empiricism and steady his practice against haphazard remedies. The healing art of Hippocrates did not yet deem itself a science; but it travelled in the light.

In concluding, mention must be made of the Hippocratic book of *Aphorisms*, — for no hand-book of medicine has ever been so thumbed through many centuries, or translated into so many languages. Its statements are pithy résumés for the guidance of the practitioner, who could not fail to be the wiser for conning them. Frequently they show astonishing insight and extraordinary knowledge. The first and most famous of them all comes as a solemn admonition, — it certainly has echoed down the ages: 'Ο βίος βραχύς, ἡ δὲ τέχνη μακρή, ὁ δὲ καιρὸς ὀξύς, ἡ δὲ πεῖρα σφαλερή, ἡ δὲ κρίσις χαλεπή:'

"Life is short and the [healing] art is long; the opportunity [to administer remedies] fleeting, experiment is dangerous, the decision difficult," and it continues: " One must not only do the the right thing oneself, but make the patient and all about him concur." What is said elsewhere might be added: " You must not only do the proper thing, but do it at the right time."

Such admonitions the young practitioner might take to heart, — and tremble!

[32]

The tone of this great aphorism [16] is in accord with Hippocrates' great and serious view of medicine and the noble calling of the physician. Futurity might well be grateful to him for the high ethics of his vast authority. Sage hints as to the physician's demeanor are given in these works. Says the little piece which is called *Nomos*, the Law or Canon: " Medicine is of all the arts the most noble; but owing to the ignorance of those who practice it . . . it is far behind the other arts. . . . As the mute figures on the stage have the shape, dress and appearance of actors, and yet are not, so physicians are many in title, but very few in reality.

" Whoever is to acquire a competent knowledge of medicine ought to have the following advantages: a natural disposition; instruction; a favorable position for the study; early tuition; love of labor; leisure. First of all, a natural talent is required, for when Nature opposes, everything else is in vain; but when Nature leads the way to what is most excellent, instruction in the art takes place, which the student must appropriate to himself by reflection, early becoming a pupil in a place well adapted for instruction. He must also bring to the task a love of labor and perseverance, so that the instruction, taking root, may bring forth proper and abundant fruits. . . .

" Possessing all these requisites to the study of medicine and having acquired a true knowledge of it, we shall thus in traveling through the cities, be esteemed physicians not in name but in reality. But inexperience is a bad treasure . . . the nurse of timidity and audacity. For timidity betrays want of powers, and audacity a want of skill." [17]

Ethically the most influential document in the history of medicine is the Hippocratic oath, still administered to the young doctors of Europe and America, though modified to suit ways of instruction which do not keep to the ancient paternal intimacy of teacher and disciple.

" I swear by Apollo the physician, and Aesculapius, and Health, and All-heal, and all the gods and goddesses, that, according to my ability and judgment, I will keep this Oath and this stipulation: to reckon him who taught me this Art equally dear to me as my parents, to share my substance with him, and relieve his necessities if required; to look upon his offspring in the same footing as my own brothers, and to teach them this Art, if they shall wish to learn it, without fee or stipulation; and that by precept, lecture, and every other mode of instruction, I will impart a knowledge of the Art to my own sons, and those of my teachers, and to disciples bound by a stipulation and oath according to the law of medicine, but to none others. I will follow that system of regimen which, according to my ability and judgment, I consider for the benefit of my patients, and abstain from whatever is deleterious and mischievous. I will give no deadly medicine to any one if asked, nor suggest any such counsel; and in like manner I will not give to a woman a pessary to produce abortion. With purity and with holiness I will pass my life and practice my Art. I will not cut persons laboring under the stone, but will leave this to be done by men who are practitioners of this work. Into whatever houses I enter, I will go into them for the benefit of the sick, and will abstain from every voluntary act of mischief and corruption; and, further, from the seduction of females or males, of freemen and slaves. Whatever, in connection with my professional practice or not in connection with it, I see or hear, in the life of men, which ought not to be spoken of abroad, I will not divulge, as reckoning that all such should be kept secret. While I continue to keep this Oath unviolated, may it be granted to me to enjoy life and the practice of the Art, respected by all men, in all times! But should I trespass and violate this Oath, may the reverse be my lot! "[18]

It is unnecessary to detail the scanty knowledge of anatomy in the Hippocratic writings or to dwell upon their ignorance of functional physiology. To such knowledge the study of the human body under dissection is essential, and probably Hippocrates and his school did not practice it. Yet they knew the positions of the internal organs, and had a good knowledge of the skeleton, of the joints and ligaments of the bones and the larger superficial muscles. They knew enough to serve the needs of their excellent surgery. Most efficient was their treatment of fractures and dislocations. The surgical treatises among the Hippocratic writings — *On Injuries of the Head, On Fractures, On Dislocations* — have evoked the praise of surgeons in all times. Although they had no special knowledge of antiseptics and asepsis, they practiced scrupulous cleanliness and understood the care of surgical patients. The efficiency of Greek surgery shows that the absence of certain specific knowledge and consequent practices now deemed essential, does not preclude wise and successful treatment.[19]

Among the Hippocratic qualities which deserve the gratitude of mankind, the first place should be given to the spirit and method of this great physician and his school, which stood fast by observation and experience, guided and systematized by large and consistent views of the actual conduct of disease. August and beneficent was the influence of this principle and method through the following six hundred years of Greek and Roman-Hellenistic medicine, closing in the work of Galen. Advance fifteen centuries further in the course of time and chequered progress, and such great physicians as Sydenham (1624–1689) and Boerhaave (1668–1738), wearied with conflicting and all-unproven medical theories, will — like many others who have been fain to do so even to our own day — be found reaching back to the method of Hippocrates.

Moreover, if the four humors have been laughed out of court, the cognate principle of correlation among the human organs with the consequent recognition of the general disorder resulting from the sickness of any one of them, is with us still. Likewise *the fundamental Hippocratic tenet of assisting nature to work her own cure* has remained valid and accepted, in some form at least of re-expression to suit the different and finally larger knowledge of later times. No one disputes it today; and it was doubly wise and sound for men whose knowledge was as pardonably rudimentary as that of Hippocrates. Charles Singer expresses his judgment of the Hippocratics thus: " The work of these men may be summed up by saying that without dissection, without any experimental physiology or pathology, and without any instrumental aid, they pushed the knowledge of the course and origin of disease as far as it is conceivable that men in such circumstances could push it. This was done as a process of pure scientific induction. Their surgery, though hardly based on anatomy, was grounded on the most carefully recorded experience. In therapeutics they allowed themselves neither to be deceived by false hopes nor led aside by vain traditions. Yet in diagnosis, prognosis, surgery and therapeutics

alike they were in many departments unsur-
passed until the nineteenth century, *and to
some of their methods we have reverted in the
twentieth. Persisting throughout the ages as a
more or less definite tradition, which attained
clearer form during and after the sixteenth
century, Hippocratic methods have formed the
basis of all departments of modern advance.*" [20]

III. ARISTOTLE'S BIOLOGY

OUR DEBT to Greek biology is not to be appraised through any attempt to trace a causal continuity between Greece and the modern world in the development of this science, or group of sciences. The continuity is problematical and lacking in causality. Modern biological science sprang from the direct investigation of the natural objects forming its provinces. Modern anatomy for instance, arose with Leonardo and Vesalius from dissections of human bodies and not from study of books. It is not to be regarded as a graft upon the ancient stock.

The fundamental aim of biology, with the Greeks and with ourselves, has been to learn about living organisms. Nevertheless, Greek biology differed from the modern biological sciences in origins and associations, in method and in temperament. Our present debt to the ancient time is owing not a little to these differences. Let us see.

In origins; — Greek science began in the large unity of the grand desire to know the constituents and processes of the world. It was pursued by men whom we have been taught to call philosophers; and in fact only gradually did philosophy, more properly speaking, differentiate itself from physics, that is, from the elemental attempt to observe and know the physical world. Greek philosophy was to consist of logical and metaphysical conceptions; Greek physical, or let us say specifically biological, science was to continue as observation and induction. Yet it did not part company from philosophy, and occasionally employed the same processes of logic and even metaphysics. The same men might still be both scientists and philosophers — or metaphysicians. The greatest of Greek biologists was very nearly the greatest of Greek philosophers; and Aristotle the biologist did not abjure the logical and metaphysical reasonings of Aristotle the philosopher.[21]

But modern biology, if we fix our eyes upon its most fecund inceptions and vigorous growth, was departmental or special from the beginning, and alien from those sweeping explanations and ultimate accountings which seemed to constitute philosophy. In this sense, neither Leonardo nor Vesalius nor Harvey was a philosopher; [22] and though Descartes, a great philosopher, followed the investigations of Harvey and dissected animals, his work along these lines was unimportant.

The origins of Greek biology correspond with its methods and its intellectual temper and predilections. Assuredly it did observe, and observed primarily, the objects or matters which attracted Greek attention. Heraclitus and Aristotle might bid men not to scorn to notice humble, even disgusting, things. But usually it was the objects which were most noticeable and alive that caught the Greek attention, like the quick and cunning animals whose acts and natures might throw some light upon man himself, in whom the Greek was interested most of all. In accord, moreover, with its origins, Greek biology sought for broad and satisfying facts or truths, such as appealed to the Greek reasoning mind. And the Greek mind, like the Greek hand, was a little impatient of drudgery. It was predisposed to accept data which satisfied its love of order and symmetry and reason and its desire to find these qualities in nature. Hence it failed to make experiments and cautiously to verify what it observed or desired to observe.

Greek biology presents penetrating descriptions which often are close and correct. The descriptions were such as yielded explanations. The *why* was always lurking, or pressing unconcealed behind the *how*, and even instigating it. The wish for explanation is the antecedent in all science; — in Greek biology it might color the description. So the description, like the wished-for explanation, was a little over-likely to accord with the insistencies of the Greek mind. But so penetrating was the insight of that mind, and so mighty its impulse toward an explanatory ordering of things, that the lesson and example of its accomplishment have not ceased to be the inspiration of the intellectual world. This is as true of Greek science as of Greek philosophy with which it was so closely related.

The beginnings of Greek biology were noticed before, in speaking of the Hippocratic school of medicine. Its matured character can best be illustrated from the works of its mightiest exponent, Aristotle. His three great biological treatises, or compendia, or perhaps note-books, may be drawn on — the *Historia Animalium*, the *De Partibus Animalium*, and the *De Generatione Animalium;* [23] then more briefly, the *Enquiry Into Plants* of his pupil Theophrastus.[24]

Aristotle's prodigious legacy of biological, or let us say zoölogical, knowledge has often been commented on, criticized, and appraised; his extraordinary insight and grasp of veritable, frequently intricate and difficult facts have been made clear and the errors (however arising) in his writings exposed. Usually one can tell when his knowledge is derived from the reports of other men, and when he has gained it from his own observation of animals, and especially from the many dissections which he must have performed. That he dissected whatever animals he could lay hands on is proved by his knowledge of their parts; but he rarely refers to his dissections [25] any more than to the method and manner of his researches generally. It is results or conclusions that are given in these writings, whether by Aristotle himself or some pupil.[26]

From the first the reader is impressed with Aristotle's comprehensive desire to order and classify the objects of his study. He would distinguish the parts of animals and arrange the animals themselves by genera and species, constantly seeking an order of progression corresponding to the excellence and amplitude of the equipment of each group of animals. The opening description, or division, of the parts of animals is so reduced to its simplest terms, and therefore so abstract that effort is needed to perceive its significance.

" Of the parts of animals some are simple: to wit, all such as divide into parts uniform with themselves, as flesh into flesh; others are composite, such as divide into parts not uniform with themselves, as, for instance, the hand does not divide into hands nor the face into faces." This distinction held good in Aristotle's time as now; [27] but the depth of its validity has been plumbed only through modern microscopic study of cells and tissues.

So in regard to the classification of animals by genera and species which may be drawn from his writings. Altogether Aristotle refers to about five hundred and forty animals of all kinds, including insects; and yet modern zoölogy, recognizing more nearly one million species, largely preserves his classification.

The attribute of soul or life and the degree and kinds of its efficient presence are with Aristotle the criterion of excellence in living

[45]

organisms: by the possession of a soul or an organic life with nutritive faculty, a plant is superior to a stone; by the possession of a soul or an organic life, with sensitive, appetitive and motor faculties (besides the nutritive), an animal is superior to a plant; and by the addition of the intellectual faculty in his soul or organic life, man is supreme among animals.

As another and concomitant test of excellence, Aristotle took the amount of vital heat which the animal possessed. " The more perfect are those which are hotter in their nature and have more moisture and are not earthy in their composition, and the measure of natural heat is the lung when it has blood in it, for generally those animals which have a lung are hotter than those which have it not, and in the former class again those whose lung is not spongy nor solid nor containing only a little blood, but soft and full of blood." [28]

These tests of excellence might be difficult to apply to the classification of animals into genera and species,— a yearning for which with a realization of its practical and logical difficulties, pervades Aristotle's biological treatises, as already said. It will be interesting to feel our way along his various avenues of approach to this many-sided problem, proceeding very tentatively with a suspicion that after all we may be following not his mental processes, but our own.

Undoubtedly a comprehensive examination of living organisms (animals rather than plants are in Aristotle's mind) must embrace the processes of formation of each animal, as well as of its characters when formed. He bids us remember that abstractions cannot form the subject of a natural science, and individual animals are the real existences, and not the genera formed by the mind. It is with individuals that we have to deal, when trying to study their formation and characteristics and even when trying to form groups of genera and species. Thus he insists upon the concrete as the real object of study; yet he groups and classifies and seeks ever the general qualities in these concrete existences — even as he did in his famous theory of tragedy, in the *Poetics*, — and one should not draw back from the humblest details provided they lead us on and disclose the great design. Therefore:

" Having already treated of the celestial world, as far as our conjectures could reach, we proceed to treat of animals, without omitting to the best of our ability any member of the kingdom, however ignoble. For if some have no graces to charm the sense, yet even these, by disclosing to intellectual perception the artistic spirit that designed them, give immense pleasure to all who can trace links of causation, and are inclined to philosophy. . . . We therefore must not recoil with childish aversion from the examination of the humbler animals. Every realm of nature is marvellous . . . so we should venture on the study of every kind of animal without distaste; for each and all will reveal to us something natural and something beautiful. Absence of the haphazard and conduciveness of everything to an end are to be found in Nature's works in the highest degree, and the resultant end of her generations and combinations is a form of the beautiful.

" If any person thinks the examination of the rest of the animal kingdom an unworthy task, he must hold in like dis-esteem the study of man. For no one can look at the *primordia* of the human frame — blood, flesh, bones, vessels, and the like — without much repugnance. Moreover, when any one of the parts or structures, be it which it may, is under dis-

cussion, it must not be supposed that it is its
material composition to which attention is
being directed or which is the object of the
discussion, but the relation of such part to the
total form. Similarly, the true object of architecture is not bricks, mortar, or timber, but the
house; and so the principal object of natural
philosophy is not the material elements, but
their composition, and the totality of the
form, independently of which they have no
existence." [29]

So the concrete part or element, or possibly
the individual animal, presents small intellectual interest by itself, but only as it contributes
to the whole and exhibits the beautiful design.
Aristotle examines individuals to discover their
common attributes; for his real interest leaps
to the group. And so he continues immediately
after the last words quoted from him: " The
course of exposition must be first to state the
attributes common to whole groups of animals,
and then to attempt to give their explanation."
That is to say, we have first to describe the
phenomena presented by each group, and
afterwards state the causes of those phenomena
and deal with their coming into existence.

There is law and purpose behind the formation of every animal and every part of an animal, since everything that nature makes is a means to an end, and nature does nothing in vain. "It is evident that there must be something or other really existing, corresponding to what we call by the name of Nature. For a given germ does not give rise to any chance living being, nor spring from any chance one; but each germ springs from a definite parent and gives rise to a definite progeny. And thus it is the germ that is the ruling influence and fabricator of the offspring." [30]

The classification of living beings should take account, it would seem, both of their characteristics and of the processes by which they and their characteristics came into existence. In either case nature herself makes no break, admits no gap, in the whole scale of animate and inanimate being: "Nature proceeds little by little from things lifeless to animal life in such a way that it is impossible to determine the exact line of demarcation, nor on which side thereof an intermediate form should be. Thus, next after lifeless things in the upward scale comes the plant, and of plants one will differ from another as to its amount of apparent vitality; and in a word, the whole genus of plants, whilst it is devoid of life as compared with an animal, is endowed with life as compared with other corporeal entities. Indeed, as we first remarked, there is observed in plants a continuous scale of ascent towards the animal. So in the sea, there are certain objects concerning which one would be at a loss to determine whether they be animal or vegetable. For instance, certain of these objects [e.g. sponges] are fairly rooted, and in several cases perish if detached. . . . Indeed, broadly speaking, the entire genus of testaceans has a resemblance to vegetables, if they be contrasted with such animals as are capable of progression.

" In regard to sensibility, some animals give no indication whatsoever of it, whilst others indicate it but indistinctly. Further, the substance of some of these intermediate creatures is fleshlike . . . but the sponge is in every respect like a vegetable. And so throughout the entire animal scale there is a graduated differentiation in amount of vitality and in capacity for motion.

" A similar statement holds good with regard to habits of life. Thus of plants that spring from seed the one function seems to be the reproduction of their own particular species, and the sphere of action with certain animals is similarly limited. The faculty of reproduction, then, is common to all alike. If sensibility be superadded, then their lives will differ from one another in respect to sexual intercourse through the varying amount of pleasure derived therefrom, and also in regard to modes of parturition and the ways of rearing their young. Some animals, like plants, simply procreate their own species at different seasons; other animals busy themselves also in procuring food for their young, and after they are reared quit them and have no further dealings with them; other animals are more intelligent and endowed with memory, and they live with their offspring for a longer period and on a more social footing.

" The life of animals, then, may be divided into two acts, — procreation and feeding; for on these two acts all their interests and life concentrate. Their food depends chiefly on the substance of which they are severally constituted; for the source of their growth in all cases will be this substance. And whatever is in conformity with nature is pleasant, and all animals pursue pleasure in keeping with their nature." [31]

These famous passages may be taken as indicating Aristotle's view of the graded ordering of life, with reference to the phenomena exhibited by living beings after they are formed. The processes of their generation were likewise graded in accordance with the nature of the animal. This graded change in the manner of generation, more than any other fact, seems to have determined Aristotle's classification of animals.

Doubtless a similarity in obvious organic structure led men to recognize the larger natural divisions, like birds and fishes. Such generic likenesses, with due account taken of evident as well as more subtle differences, might be followed in forming conceptions of subordinate groups. But to the mind searching for criterions of identity or distinction, nothing is more taking than the ways in which animals reproduce their kind. So felt this profound student of life. Perhaps no other man has ever discovered so many interesting facts touching the production of the young within and without the womb. Of course he stood but at the threshold of embryology. He had no microscope. The myriad facts which the studies of the last two centuries have elicited were unknown to him for the most part — but not altogether, since now and then the modern investigator " discovers " what Aristotle knew. Yet whole provinces of the considerations of modern biology scarcely touched him. All the more marvellous were the forward thrusts of his mind toward what the distant future should make clear. One of those thrustings forward was the classification of animals, which may be drawn from his writings.

His fundamental division was into animals with blood and animals without, that is to say, those who have no true blood but a different fluid performing a like nutritive function. This division coincides with the modern one into vertebrates and invertebrates, ascribed to Lamarck (1744–1829). Through the constituent groups under both divisions will be found a series of gradations in foetal development within the parent's body; and these determine the Aristotelian group formation.

Man, the Cetacea, viviparous quadrupeds, birds, reptiles, fishes, bony and then cartilaginous, come within the division of animals with blood. Aristotle had no conception of the mammalian ovum, and consequently regarded the embryo of mammals as born alive within

[54]

the womb, and as living in a fuller sense (or with more kinds of life) than could be ascribed to an egg. In the three lower orders of blooded animals, the young developed from an egg; hence these were essentially oviparous, although the egg might hatch within the mother and the young come forth alive, as is the case of certain sharks. Such animals were externally viviparous, yet the young began as an egg and not as a living foetus.

In the grounds of this classification there was fundamental error, arising from Aristotle's ignorance of the mammalian egg, and yet much penetrating observation, the results of which still hold. His work upon the chick of the domestic fowl, and his extraordinary anticipatory description of the gestation of certain sharks are examples. In his method of close continuous study of the chick developing within the egg, he may have been preceded by the writer of one of the Hippocratic tracts.[32]

" Generation from the egg proceeds in an identical manner with all birds, but the full periods from conception to birth differ. . . . With the common hen, after three days and three nights, there is the first indication of the embryo . . . the heart appears like a speck of

[55]

blood in the white of the egg. This point beats and moves as though endowed with life, and from it two vein-ducts with blood in them trend in a convoluted course; and a membrane carrying bloody fibres now envelops the yolk, leading off from the vein-ducts. A little afterwards the body is differentiated, at first very small and white. The head is clearly distinguished, and in it the eyes, swollen out to a great extent. . . ." [33]

Without carrying further our citation on the chick, we may remark that Aristotle saw all that can be seen without a microscope. His description of the gestation of the placental sharks makes too difficult a matter for a layman to set forth for other laymen. I will borrow the account given by an Aristotelian scholar who is himself a biologist.

" There is perhaps no chapter in the *Historia Animalium* more attractive to the anatomist than one which deals with the anatomy and mode of reproduction of the cartilaginous fishes, the sharks and rays, a chapter which moved to admiration that prince of anatomists, Johannes Müller. The latter wrote a volume [*Ueber den glatten Hai des Aristoteles*, Berlin, 1842] on the text of a page of Aristotle, a page packed full of a multitude of facts, in no one of which did Johannes Müller discover a flaw. The subject is technical, but the gist of the matter is this: that among the Selachians (as, after Aristotle, we still sometimes call them) there are many diversities in the structure of the parts in question, and several distinct modes in which the young are brought forth and matured. For in many kinds an egg is laid, which eggs, by the way, Aristotle describes with great minuteness. Other kinds do not lay eggs, but bring forth their young alive, and these include the Torpedo and numerous sharks or dogfish. The egg-shell is in these cases very thin, and breaks before the birth of the young. But among them there are a couple of sharks, of which one species was within Aristotle's reach, where a very curious thing happens. Through the delicate membrane, which is all that is left of the egg-shell, the great yolk-sac of the embryo becomes connected with the parental tissues, which infold and interweave with it; and by means of this temporary union the blood of the parent becomes the medium of nourishment for the young. And the whole arrangement is physiologically identical with what obtains in the

[57]

higher animals, the mammals, or warm-blooded vivipara. It is true that the yolk-sac is not identical with that other embryonic membrane which comes in the mammals to discharge the function of which I speak; but Aristotle was aware of the difference, and distinguishes the two membranes with truth and accuracy.

" It happens that of the particular genus of sharks to which this one belongs, there are two species differing by almost imperceptible characters; but it is in one only of the two, the γαλεὸς λεῖος of Aristotle, that this singular phenomenon of the *placenta vitellina* is found. It is found in the great blue shark of the Atlantic and the Mediterranean; but this creature grows to a very large size before it breeds, and such great specimens are not likely to have come under Aristotle's hands. Cuvier (1769–1832) detected the phenomenon in the blue shark, but paid little attention to it, and, for all his knowledge of Aristotle, did not perceive that he was dealing with an important fact which the Philosopher had studied and explained. In the seventeenth century, the anatomist Steno (1638–86) actually rediscovered the phenomenon, in the γαλεὸς λεῖος, the *Mustelus laevis* itself, but he was

unacquainted with Aristotle. And the very
fact was again forgotten until Johannes Müller
brought it to light, and showed not only how
complete was Aristotle's account, but how wide
must have been his survey of this class of
fishes to enable him to record this peculiarity
in its relation to their many differences of
structure and reproductive habit." [34]

Turning from animals with blood to the
bloodless animals, Aristotle continues his
attempt to guide himself by the descending
methods of reproduction, which correspond
with the lowering degrees of life and vital
function in these inferior but still marvellously
interesting creatures.   Passing   downwards
through those *Crustacea* which he finds generated from an imperfect ovum, he enters the
realm of insects. These spring from the
scolex or grub, which is metamorphosed, passing through the chrysalis or *pupa*, into the
perfect insect.[35] Lowest in the scale are
molluscs and finally the zoöphytes (sponges,
Coelenterates) which are produced from
generative slime or by spontaneous generation. The last idea, of course, has been
abandoned.

Instead of giving the further details of

Aristotle's orders of animals, I quote the critical résumé of a recent authority:

" The classification of birds is to this day in an unstable state. We may say that Aristotle's grouping is substantially that which prevailed in scientific works till recent times and still remains as the popular division. His separation of the cartilaginous from the bony fishes, on the other hand, still stands in scientific works, and is a stroke of genius which must have been reached by means of careful dissection. . . .

" For the *Anaima* [bloodless] or Invertebrates even modern systems of classification are but tentative. There is an enormous number of species, and after centuries of research naturalists still find vast gaps even in the field of mere naked-eye observation. Nevertheless, with the instinct of genius, and with only some 240 of these forms on which to work, Aristotle has fastened on some of the most salient points. Especially brilliant is his treatment of the Molluscs. There can be no doubt that he dissected the bodies and carefully watched the habits of octopuses and squids, *Malacia* as he calls them. He separates them too far from the other Molluscs grouped by him as *Ostracoderma,* but his actual descriptions of the structure of the Cephalopods are exceedingly remarkable. His distinctions between the *Malacostraca* or Crustacea, *Entoma,* Sponges, and Jellyfish are also still of value, and these divisions remain along much the same lines as he left them." [30]

In reading through the biological treatises of Aristotle, one realizes that they are the pioneerings of a mighty mind. He was laying out the multitudinous matter, striving, not indeed to introduce an order not its own into the *chaos* of Nature, but rather to apprehend and describe and know the reason of the intricate and marvelous order which was embodied in Nature's realm. That Nature held such order, and presented it and worked ever with purpose in fulfilling it, was Aristotle's scientific and philosophic faith. If Anaxagoras or another had this faith before him, he was to render it explicit through a more adequate analysis, a keener discrimination, and a marshalling of detail hitherto unattempted. He was a universal pioneer in nature's vast realm: an investigating and dissecting pioneer, pressing on through all the seeming mazes of the unexplored jungle, insistent upon laying out or rather discovering the paths of Nature's ordering. Thus he was a pioneer of natural science. But the intellectual needs of the philosopher drove him to another and more ultimate kind of pioneering. He must think the matter out, and find the logical, even the metaphysical basis of justification of his apprehension of Nature's processes: he must adjust his knowledge of Nature to the demands of his thought and possibly constrain it to the categories of his metaphysics.[37] Let us follow him, for a little, here.

Aristotle proceeds to attack the basic *how* and *why* of living things. His treatment of these organisms — that is, his biology — did not call for a discussion of the world's material, but merely its adaptability to nature's purposes. But his treatment did demand a discriminating conception of causation in order to understand how plants and animals came to be what they were. Although his analysis of the four kinds of causes is familiar, we may note the application made of it in his biology.

" There are four causes underlying everything: first, the final cause, that for the sake of which a thing exists; secondly, the formal cause, the definition of its essence (and these

[62]

two we may regard pretty much as one and the same); thirdly, the material; and fourthly, the moving principle or efficient cause." [38]

"Now that with which the ancient writers, who first philosophized about nature, busied themselves, was the material principle and the material cause. They inquired what this is, and what its character; how the universe is generated out of it, and by what motor influence, whether, for instance, by antagonism or friendship, whether by intelligence or spontaneous action,[39] — the substratum of matter being assumed to have certain inseparable properties; fire, for instance, to have a hot nature, earth, a cold one; the former to be light, the latter heavy. For even the genesis of the universe is thus explained by them. After a like fashion they deal with the development of plants and of animals. They say, for instance, that the water contained in the body causes by its currents the formation of the stomach and the other receptacles of food or of excretion; and that the breath by its passage breaks open the outlets of the nostrils; air and water being the materials of which bodies are made; for all represent nature as composed of such or similar substances.

" But if men and animals and their several parts are natural phenomena, then the natural philosopher must take into consideration not merely the ultimate substances of which they are made, but also flesh, bone, blood, and all the other homogeneous parts; not only these, but also the heterogeneous parts, such as face, hand, foot; and must examine how each of these comes to be what it is, and in virtue of what force. For to say what are the ultimate substances out of which an animal is formed ... is no more sufficient that would be a similar account in the case of a couch or the like. For we should not be content to say that the couch was made of bronze or wood, but should try to describe its design or mode of composition in preference to material; or, if we deal with the material, it would at any rate be with the concretion of material and form. For a couch is such and such a form embodied in this or that matter, or such and such matter with this or that form; so that its shape and structure must be included in our description. For the formal nature is of greater importance than the material nature."

Aristotle then shows, on the other hand, that shape and color do not make the essence of an animal or its parts: a dead body is not a man, nor a bronze hand a hand, nor the eye in a dead body really an eye. Rather, to describe an animal, one must show what it actually is in substance as well as form; and so with its several organs. He then argues that it is the soul or life which constitutes the essential nature of the animal. For "nature is spoken of in two senses, and the nature of a thing is either its matter or its essence; nature as essence including both the motor cause and the final cause. Now it is in the latter of these two senses that either the whole soul or some part of it constitutes the nature of an animal."

Nature always seeks an end, — a famous Aristotelian statement; and the end is the final cause, which in the case of animals is the soul or the life of the animal, the full functioning of its nature. Logically, that is, in thought, this final cause or end is prior to the motor cause; "For this is the Reason, and the Reason forms the starting point, alike in the works of art and in works of nature." With a builder the final cause is the construction of a house; in nature it is the making of an animal. " In the works of nature the good end and the final cause is still more dominant than in works of art." So it constitutes the nature of the animal or the nature of an organ more than the material of its body or the necessary processes of its growth or natural formation do.[40] [Yet] " in order of time, the material and the generative process must necessarily be anterior to the being that is generated; but in logical order the definitive character and form of each being precedes the material."

" But Nature flies from the infinite," says Aristotle in consonance with his Greek temperament, and, thinking of the literally unending confusion that would result if parents did not produce offspring of the same kind with themselves, he says: " for the infinite is unending or imperfect, and Nature ever seeks an end." [41]

So universal Nature, or Nature in the large, and so the nature of the individual animal. As for the natural philosopher, he would be but a crude teleologist, with but a crude notion of the working of final cause, that is, of plan and purposeful utility, did he not find this plan and use in every detail of the animal structure. Since the soul, or life, or the full living functioning is the end or object of each individual animal, it must direct and mould the growth and character of every part. Aristotle holds this creed, and devotes the *De Partibus Animalium* to its special illustration.

First he shows it generally in regard to the animal's component parts. The homogeneous fluids and tissues exist for the sake of the more especially active parts or organs,[42] like the eye or hand. They must possess the different properties, like fluidity, softness, or hardness, required by the organ, and of which it will present a combination. "For the hand . . . requires one property to enable it to effect pressure, and another and different property for simple prehension. For this reason the active or executive parts of the body are compounded out of bones, sinews, flesh and the like, but not these latter out of the former." And the relations between these two orders of parts are determined by a final cause,[43] which is the life of the whole animal.

Aristotle will not flinch from the principle that this final end, the life of the whole animal, calls every part into being. It is irrational to hold the reverse, i.e., that the character or mechanical power of a part produces or determines that final end which is the life or soul with its distinguishing properties. The motor or efficient cause must be subordinate to the final cause, and never the reverse.

To illustrate by a famous instance: " Standing thus erect, man has no need of legs in front, and in their stead has been endowed by nature with arms and hands. Now it is the opinion of Anaxagoras that the possession of these hands is the cause of man being of all animals the most intelligent. But it is more rational to suppose that his endowment with hands is the consequence rather than the cause of his superior intelligence. For the hands are instruments or organs, and the invariable plan of nature in distributing the organs is to give each to such animal as can make use of it; nature acting in this matter as any prudent man would do. . . . We must conclude that man does not owe his superior intelligence to his hands, but his hands to his superior intelligence." [44]

Modern biology finds other factors entering this problem, which is part of a large controversy still. Our biologists might not decide for Aristotle here, yet would be well disposed toward another deduction which he drew from his teleological creed: aberrant or occasional

characters, not common to the species, are not
due to a final cause; that is to say, they are
not useful or conducive to the end which is the
life of the animal.

" For whenever things are not the product
of Nature working upon the animal kingdom
as a whole, nor yet characteristic of each
separate kind, then none of these things is such
as it is or is so developed for any final cause.
The eye, for instance, exists for a final cause,
but it is not blue for a final cause unless this
condition be characteristic of the kind of
animal."

In other words, when a character is common
to all animals of an established group, then it
exists for a purpose; but fluctuating characters
are not so developed. Such characters have
" no connection with the essence of the animal's
being, but we must refer the causes to the
material and the motive principle or efficient
cause, on the view that these things come into
being by necessity." Apparently Aristotle
means that the formal or final cause cannot
always control the material and the efficient
causes, and variations from the perfect type
arise.[45]

Every animal with its essential or constant

parts, is fashioned by its final cause through a process of generation. Even when mature, it is not a static being, but still a vital process, living its life, its full life which it had not attained as an embryo. The embryo has the nutritive soul or life, but not the sensitive and motor soul which comes at birth, and still less the rational soul which comes to man alone.

" For nobody would put down the unfertilized embryo as soulless or in every sense bereft of life (since both the semen and the embryo of an animal have every bit as much life as a plant). . . . That then they possess the nutritive soul is plain. . . . As they develop, they also acquire the sensitive soul, in virtue of which an animal is an animal. . . . An animal does not become at the same time an animal and a man and a horse or any other particular animal. For the end is developed last, and the peculiar character of the species is the end of the generation of each individual." [46] *This passage states a fundamental principle of embryology, that the general characters belonging to the class or genus are first displayed by the embryo, and afterwards the distinguishing characters of the species to which it belongs.* [47]

So the embryo has not all the characters of the species from the beginning, nor does it possess its full endowment of soul or life, but develops gradually. Its development continues after birth, — the child exhibiting a larger proportion of generic animal qualities, and a less proportion of those distinctly human:

"In the great majority of animals there are traces of psychical qualities or attitudes, which qualities are more markedly differentiated in the case of human beings. For just as we pointed out resemblances in physical organs, so in a number of animals we observe gentleness or fierceness, courage or timidity, fear or confidence, high spirit or low cunning, and with regard to intelligence, something equivalent to sagacity. Some of these qualities in man, as compared with the corresponding qualities in animals, differ only quantitatively. . . . [This] will be more clearly apprehended if we regard the phenomena of childhood; for in children may be observed the traces and seeds of what will one day be settled psychological habits, though psychologically a child hardly differs for the time being from an animal; so that one is quite justified in saying that, as regards man and animals, certain psychical qualities are identical with one another, whilst others resemble, and others are analogous to each other." [48]

It was evident to Aristotle that the nutritive and motor life or soul could not exist without the body: "Plainly those principles whose activity is bodily cannot exist without a body, e.g., walking cannot exist without feet. For the same reason they cannot enter from outside. . . ." But the final problem, — "a question of the greatest difficulty," says Aristotle, — is: "When and how and whence is a share in reason acquired by those animals that participate in this principle?" His answer is, that, unlike the nutritive and motor life, the reason, the rational soul, alone enters from without and "alone is divine, for no bodily activity has any connexion with the activity of reason."

Modern biological psychology might not agree. Yet Aristotle's psychology was biological through and through. The soul with him was life; and life in its plant and animal activity was in and of the body and inseparable from it, save that only reason, the higher mind of man, was not of the body, but was divine. We still ask, what is divine? What is the body? What is reason?

To return for a moment to some Aristotelian opinions bearing on the generation of life and its transmission of attributes to offspring. He combated pangenesis, the theory that the semen must come from the whole body, in order to account for the inheritance of so many diverse individual resemblances.[49] He was aware that bodily imperfections incidentally acquired would not be inherited, like congenital traits. Yet he realized the constitutional effects arising from the alteration of a small part or organ: that if animals " be subjected to a modification in minute organs, they are liable to immense modifications in their general configuration," — a phenomenon noticeable with gelded animals.[50] Hippocrates had shown how often trouble with one organ worked a general disturbance of the system. Aristotle recognized also that the habits of animals are connected with their main functions of " breeding and the rearing of young, or with procuring a due supply of food; and these habits are modified so as to suit cold and heat and the variations of the season." [51] He has much to say of migration and hibernation.

In ancient natural science the manner of

approach, and more assuredly the phraseology, may be strange to us, and at first sight seem to represent exceedingly fantastic views. But on deeper consideration, remembering our own actual confusion of thought as to the nature of life and the powers or qualities through which living organisms are alive, sometimes we see that, if we will but change the ancient phrases a little, we shall not find the underlying thought as alien as it seemed. State the ancient hypotheses a little differently, give them a slight push, see them from another angle, and they will often parallel modern conceptions, themselves admittedly unattached to basic considerations, and therefore, perhaps, insecurely founded. This reflection applies to many of the Hippocratic concepts, to many a view of Aristotle and, as we may hereafter see, to the genially eclectic system of Galen.

One must not make an evolutionist of Aristotle. But if the world of plants and animals was not for him an evolution of species in the modern sense, he recognized most pregnantly its graded continuity. This unbroken gradation pervaded the process of embryonic growth, as well as the completed structure of mature organs. Still more subtly it followed the increments of soul or life, possessed by each organism next higher in the universal series. Organic nature presented an ascending scale.

If this organic world was not an evolution strictly speaking, it was not static. It was alive, in vital process, pressing on toward self-fulfillment through the purposeful power of nature. Each animal was formed and conducted to its end by the soul or life which was its purpose and design, its final cause. In like manner each organ was adapted to its function. The plastic power of serviceableness, of utility and use, the formation and existence of all parts as means to ends, with Nature ever working toward an end and doing nothing vainly, — these convictions were launched by the great Stagyrite upon the mighty rôles they were to play in all the subsequent thinking of mankind. For " barren virgins," final causes were to have a large progeny!

The principles of Aristotle are not dead. Changed scarcely in form, conceptions of the vital power of Nature have ever filled the minds of men and still live in the minds of those men of science for whom mechanics and chemistry cannot explain the world of life. Specific teleological explanations of function are easily overthrown; and such, generically, may be doomed. Yet life remains, very formative, apparently still purposeful, still tending toward self-fulfillment. The vital principle is utterly wonderful and elusive, a will-o'-the-wisp, and yet assuredly there. Anatomists, physiologists, biologists, even physicists, are not quite without it. Some among them crave such an explanatory principle " to save the phenomena! " Though it lead into swamps of mysticism, people will not give it up and be satisfied with mechanics and chemistry. The fact of life is the prime organic reality: it is still utterly wonderful and elusive, and yet assuredly there. While biology today works largely with mechanical and chemical data, and uses mechanistic and chemical hypotheses, the majority of biologists recognize that such data and such principles do not afford a sufficient explanation or description of living organisms.

Seeing that chemical and mechanistic formulae give no real picture of the organism, many biologists still think that no real picture of it can be reached through such channels exclusively. There is still much Aristotelianism in modern physiology. As Aristotle held that the material and moving causes yield no adequate conception of the organism, so biology today inclines to hold that no adequate description of the living organism can be framed in categories of " matter " and " energy."

Phrases change; and thinking takes a new direction from the new phrase and seems to flow in untried channels. The old phrase becomes an alien. Few of us today could bring ourselves to accept *eo nomine* the ψυχή, — the soul or, if one will, the organic life in its ascending scale, — as the *entelechy*, to wit, " the form or actuality of a natural body having in it the capacity of life." More specifically, the ψυχή is the " first entelechy," or actuality, standing as knowledge stands to the exercise of knowledge in speculation. This " soul " is the formative principle of the body and the body's end or final cause, even as speculative activity (τὸ θεωρεῖν) is the soul's final end.

Such statements are not of our time. Yet perhaps they are not so far from our intellectual purposes. Do we not think that all the sciences, including those having to do with organisms, contribute to the soul which is life, and indeed the highest life which is of the mind? This is the Aristotelian view, and one properly belonging to a man who saw life whole and realized the splendor of its manifestations, beyond the fields of science, in art and literature, in tragedy and epic poetry. The " end " of the body is the human personality made up not only of its intellectual strainings, but of its nobler impulses and more sublime emotions, the sense of holiness and beauty and other unanalyzable things of human experience.

And as for the example of Aristotle, though he be prone to leap to principles from insufficient grounds, and though his methods were not those of modern scientific verification, still *the largeness and penetration of his views, his constant envisaging of each detail as part of a greater living whole, his insistence upon the ultimate bearings of each fact,* all this still has at least some echo of inspiration even for a time when the vast complexity of research forces most scholars, as well as scientists, into a sort of rodent specialism. Before him no one had so grandly and so profoundly seen the organism as a whole and as a coördination of parts, and few men since his time.

Aristotle's work on Plants is not extant. To judge from the passages touching this subject, which are scattered through his other works,[52] his botanical observations were less penetrating than his zoölogical. Yet it is not well to judge him from these fragments, when his main work is lost. We pass at once to the writings of his but slightly younger disciple, Theophrastus.

The latter's *Enquiry Into Plants* [53] is the great classical botany, and is more clearly written and better put together than his *De Causis Plantarum*.[54] No more than Aristotle himself, is Theophrastus to be taken as the first botanist. Much thought had already been devoted to plant life and to the medical properties of plants, for instance, by the Hippocratic school. His work is far from primitive, yet the author still wanders in a maze, since he has not reached a satisfactory or, so to speak, " natural " system of classification. Here Greek botany remained behind Greek zoölogy, and one may say at once that the *Enquiry Into Plants* has by no means the philosophical interest of Aristotle's works on zoölogy, nor is it as suggestive or useful for the modern student. Indeed, the view of at least one able historian of botany would seem to be that the botanical ideas of both master and pupil had not an altogether favorable effect upon the progress made by that science, say, from the sixteenth century onwards.[55]

Theophrastus would not have been the pupil of his master had he not been impressed with the luring analogies and even continuities observed by Aristotle, between the vegetable and animal kingdoms. In fact these observed — or ill-observed — resemblances or analogies not infrequently led him astray, whatever breadth of view they gave him.

For example: "The primary and most important parts, which are also common to most [plants], are these, root, stem, branch, twig; these are the parts into which we might divide the plant, regarding them as members, corresponding to the members of animals; for each of these is distinct in character from the rest, and together they make up the whole."[56]

He saw, however, that "we must not assume that in all respects there is complete correspondence between plants and animals. And that is why the number also of parts is indeterminate; for a plant has the power of growth in all its parts, inasmuch as it has life in all its parts; wherefore we should regard them not for what they are but for what they are about to be." [57]

Theophrastus realizes the intricate complexity of his subject and that a true classification of plants is beyond him: " In fact your plant is a thing various and manifold, and so it is difficult to describe in general terms; in proof whereof we have the fact that we cannot here seize on any universal character which is common to all, as a mouth and a stomach are common to all animals. . . . For not all plants have root, stem, branch, twig, leaf, flower or fruit, or again bark, core, fibres, or veins; for instance, fungi and truffles; and yet these and such like characters belong to a plant's essential nature. However . . . these characters belong especially to trees, and our classification of characters belongs more particularly to these; and it is right to make these the standard, in treating of the others." [58]

With other ancient writers Theophrastus was much intrigued by conceptions of differences of sex between plants. He did not understand the sexual parts of flowers. With reference to palms, he comes nearest to an idea of the process of fertilization, knowing of long-established practices in their cultivation. He says that the " male " and the " female " have been distinguished with all trees, " the latter being fruit-bearing, the former barren in some kinds." [59]

" With dates, it is helpful to bring the male to the female; for it is the male which causes the fruit to persist and ripen. . . . The process is thus performed: when the male palm is in flower, they at once cut off the spathe on which the flower is, just as it is, and shake the bloom with the flower and the dust over the fruit of the female, and, if this is done to it, it retains the fruit and does not shed it." [60]

Without following Theophrastus further, I will borrow a summary of his botanical achievements, or rather of his position, from one more competent than myself:

" 1. He distinguished the external organs of plants, naming them in regular sequence from root to fruit, and attained in many cases to a really philosophical distinction.

" 2. He definitely set forth the leaf homology of the perianth members of flowers but attained to no real knowledge of their sexual nature.

" 3. He established the first rudiments of a botanical nomenclature.

" 4. He watched the development of seeds and was able to some extent to distinguish between dicotyledons and monocotyledons.

" 5. He established a relationship between structure and habits, and approaches the conception of geographical distribution.

" 6. He saw the need for a general classification of plants and made some attempt at a system, though he failed to produce one which was in fact workable.

" 7. *He perceived a general relation between structure and function in plants, and thus laid the basis of scientific botany.*" [61]

IV. PROGRESS IN ANATOMY AND
MEDICINE

IT IS by an easy transition that we turn from biology to medicine, from pure science inspired by the sheer desire to know and account for living organisms, to the healing art, which may be also scientific, though led by practical beneficent intent. The transition is the easier because we are in the later fourth and the third centuries before Christ, the most brilliant scientific age of Greece, though Aristotle lived no longer. Medicine in the Alexandrian school, led by Herophilus and Erasistratus, was supported by the now veritable sciences of anatomy and physiology.

And of their works only scattered fragments have survived! Admirable as these men were, we must remember that we are not engaged upon a history of Greek medicine or biology, but are thinking of the value to the moderns of what the Greeks accomplished. Therefore we must occupy ourselves chiefly with those works which have survived, as the direct vehicles of the ancient heritage; and such, above all, are the works of the Hippocratics, of Aristotle and of Galen. Hence we pass by many men, brave and good, with but slight mention. Our present task is to trace the currents of medicine and its supporting sciences through the later Greek and best Roman periods till they are gathered up into the encyclopaedic system of Galen in the latter part of the second century after Christ.[62]

In the third century before Christ, Alexandria presented such facilities and incentives for study and investigation as had never before been brought together. The first Ptolemies formed a great library covering all subjects of study, and established zoölogical parks and botanical gardens. Their munificence enabled scholars and men of science to pursue their studies; and mathematics, astronomy and physics flourished, as well as history, philology, and poetry. There were hospitals for the treatment and observation of diseases, and for perhaps a century human bodies were methodically dissected. Possibly the Egyptian custom of opening the body for embalming had dispelled the Greek aversion to mutilation of the dead. But dissection of human bodies appears to have been stopped before the close of the second century before Christ, though the dissection of dead and living animals continued.

Herophilus and Erasistratus belong to the Alexandrian period, though only the former is known to have worked in Alexandria. They were born about the year three hundred. The reputation of Herophilus has come down to us less assaulted than that of Erasistratus, whom Galen hated for his alleged mechanical view of the action of the human organs.

Herophilus was at all events the more deferential in his treatment of Hippocrates, and this was to be the test of orthodoxy in the Greco-Roman medical tradition. He did not dispute the conception of the four humors, but preferred to think of four faculties as moving the human organism, to wit, the nourishing faculty of the liver and digestive organs, the warming power of the heart, the thinking faculty of the brain, and the perceptive faculty of the nerves. Above all, this man relied upon clinical observation and the results of his dissections. He appears to have been the first to have worked through the entire human anatomy. He discerned the connection between the brain and spinal cord and the nerves which proceeded from these centres; also the connection of the digestive system with the lacteals; and by the aid of the clepsydra he made a study of pulse variations as a gauge of the patient's condition. Realizing the dangers of medical theory, he fell back upon the sound clinical methods of Hippocrates; and like the master, avoided the finely drawn distinctions of unproved diagnoses. His own further experience and his greater knowledge of anatomy were brought to bear upon his treatment of diseases, while he also made improvements in surgery and obstetrics. A great and admirable figure this Herophilus.

Less conservative and Hippocratic was Erasistratus (also a great practitioner), who would have nothing to do with the four humors or four anything. Believing that a general knowledge of the human body and its functioning in health was not necessarily of practical use to the physician, he tended to specialize in his own anatomical researches, which were, however, brilliant in result. He gave a better description of the liver and its gall ducts, and for the first time gave a correct description of the heart. He advanced the knowledge of the brain, and the distinctions between vessels and nerves, and divided the motor from the sensory nerves, — an immortal achievement. His autopsies extended the knowledge of pathological conditions of the internal organs.

Mechanical views prevailed in his physiology, in which Nature's *horror vacui* played a leading rôle. For him, the body, compounded of atoms, was vivified by warmth from without: his physiology felt the need of some explanatory principle like oxygen. The source of organic energy was two-fold, the blood propelled through the veins, and the *pneuma* " which is the energy carrier and dominates all vital phenomena. Renovation of the *pneuma* is brought about through respiration, whereby air penetrates into the left side of the heart through the pulmonary vein. Thus two varieties of *pneuma* result, of which one (the *vital pneuma*) is propelled into the arteries, its function being to regulate vegetative processes throughout the body; whilst the other (*soul-pneuma*) has the brain as its goal, whence it effects movement and sensation by way of the nervous system " (Neuburger, p. 182). One sees that Erasistratus was kept from recognizing the circulation of the blood only by the persistent ancient error that the arteries carried, not blood, but air.

He conceived illness as resulting from the loading of the parts of the organism with insufficiently digested food-matter; which prevented the organism from functioning. This made a condition of " plethora," from which resulted the various sicknesses. Thus he regarded fever (which he did not consider in itself a special disease, but a symptom) as resulting from a stoppage of the circulation of the *pneuma* in the large arteries, due to the intrusion of blood from overloaded veins. He sought to remove the " plethora " as the cause of the disease; but did not concern himself in practice with the remoter causes of the plethora itself. Thus his diagnosis was local and special, — " Cnidian " indeed, — and did not follow the larger and far-reaching lines of the Hippocratic prognosis.

It may be supposed that the therapeutic principles of Erasistratus did not lead practitioners to apply the growing knowledge of anatomy to the cure of disease. The application was too baffling. Yet the rivalry between his school and that of Herophilus brought the practice of medicine to its zenith in the years immediately following the death of the two masters. Soon, however, tendencies to simplify principles and practice intervened; and practitioners were ready enough to disburden themselves of useless knowledge.

Either through legitimate descent or from reaction, divergent medical attitudes became apparent. One must not, however, infer such opposite practices as the opposing names of these medical sects might seem to indicate, for they had much in common and tended to exemplify Greek temperance and reasonableness in the treatment of patients. Whatever was the theoretical position of his school, " there were for the wiser Greek physician three factors of safety: he was free from magic; he was a master of hygiene; and, whatever his abstract notions, he never forgot to treat the individual." (Allbutt.)

Naturally the various phases of Greek medical theory were colored, temperamentally, by the current attitudes of Greek philosophy toward nature and human life and man's knowledge of the same. So completely had Greek natural philosophy boxed the compass of possible opinion, that no medical theory could avoid adopting as its ultimate base some recognized philosophic view of the constitution of the world and of man, its denizen; for instance, the atomism of Democritus or some other philosopher's opinions as to the *psyche* or *pneuma*.

There was a school of regular sceptics in Alexandrian times, and scepticism regarding philosophic or scientific knowledge was frequent beyond their company. Many physicians were inclined to be sceptical of any medical theory. This inclination promoted empiricism and electicism in medicine. There arose a definite school of so-called Empirics, a name of their own choosing. Although rejecting theories as to the nature of disease, they were not casual experimenters with likely or foolish remedies. But there had been enough school-talk and argument; cures did not lie in such discussion. The practitioner's efficacy was to be gained from his own observations and even experiments, made with due consideration of the clinical experience recorded by others. If the case was novel, the analogies of not too dissimilar cases might apply. There were good surgeons among these Empirics, who were adding their own experience to the general store.

In the last pre-Christian centuries Greek medicine reached Rome. The native Roman practice had been of the homeliest, and accompanied always with a dose of superstition. For our purpose it is quite negligible. But some of the Latins, in medicine as well as literature, were capable of learning. Such a one was the exceedingly intelligent Celsus who, in the first half of the first Christian century, composed or translated an admirable hand-book of medicine and surgery. Whatever the sources of his materials were, he was a man of sense and discrimination, and wrote a Latin that assured his book an enthusiastic reception with the Humanists when it was re-discovered in the fifteenth century. It was printed at Florence in the year 1478, before the works of either Galen or Hippocrates.

Celsus knew the history of medicine, and in his Introduction aptly describes the sects of his time. He speaks of the Empirics, who would have nothing to do with the remote and hidden causes of disease, seeing that men always had differed regarding them; only the obvious causes were to be considered and treated. The Empirics were interested in the cure rather than in the cause. Opposed to them were those more dogmatic doctors who were not happy unless they could understand the *ratio* of men's bodies and of their disturbances. They professed a rational medicine and held it necessary to understand the antecedent and obscure, as well as the palpable, causes of the disease, and insisted upon a knowledge of anatomy. In their opinion those who best knew the constitution of the body and the causes of disease had the best chance to effect a cure. Experience was important, but must always be approached through the *ratio* of things.

Then Celsus speaks of those who adhered to the *methodum,* the simple but sufficient way, which was in fine a rather Roman simplification of Greek theory, especially of the atomic theory and its application to the constitution and diseases of the human body. In general — and the Methodists preferred generalizations to the specific knowledge which was more difficult — diseases are due to a condition of undue tension or rigidity in the body, or on the other hand to excessive relaxation. In the first case, the pores between the atoms are clogged, and in the second they are too loose and open. The theory was elastic and the treatment reasonable, consisting in warm baths and other relaxing or invigorating measures as the case seemed to require.

Expressing his own opinion, Celsus decides for a middle course, whereby medicine should rely upon experience rationally: let one treat the evident causes of the disease, and as for the remote, meditate on them. Students should learn anatomy from the bodies of the dead and from study of living and wounded men. The surgical portions of Celsus's handbook are particularly good.

Theories sat rather lightly on these excellent practitioners of the Greco-Roman time, who might call themselves by one name or another. This remark applies to members of the so-called "Pneumatic" School, who were generally eclectic, adopting the best features of medical practice in the second half of the first century. They were affected by the Stoic physics, in which borrowed materials filled out a system novel in form. Accepting the old working elements, they found the life-giving principle to be the "Pneuma," like unto air and breath. It is innate, yet constantly renewed through breathing, and circulates with the blood through the arteries and veins to all parts of the body, — the arteries conveying more *pneuma,* and the veins more blood. *Pneuma* vivifies the body, and makes it a living unity, carries on the energies of growth and reproduction, as well as of sensation, desire, and thought. The normal condition and proper τόνος or tension of the *pneuma* means health, and this is indicated by the pulse; while sickness springs from disorder of the *pneuma,* due to irregularities of the warm and cold or dry and moist elements, and the consequent morbid excess of one or the other of the humors.

While these "Pneumatics" rejected the fundamental theory of the Methodists, they availed themselves of their treatment of disease, and drew upon all the best medical knowledge of the time. They were wise physicians, following many a precept of Hippocrates, and efficient surgeons. One among them, Archigenes, a contemporary of Trajan, seems to have been extraordinarily resourceful and inventive: "what we need is to be fertile in expedients, not to be always attending to the writings of other people," said he.

Says Sir Clifford Allbutt: "The ancient Greeks shrank from mutilation; and amputation, mentioned by the Hippocratean physicians only in gangrene as a subsidiary aid, seems, even in Alexandria, to have made no great progress; for Celsus also regarded it as a last sad resource in gangrene: yet by the time of Trajan, under Archigenes, amputation had become a recognized procedure for ulcers, growths, injuries and even deformities. The limb to be removed was bandaged to expel the blood, and a tourniquet was placed above the line of severance; or sometimes the chief blood-vessels were first cut down and tied, and the smaller tied or twisted, during the operation — 'transfixing them with a sharp hook and twisting them round and round and closing them by this twisting' — a proceeding of which there is no trace in Hippocrates, nor apparently in the earlier Alexandria. These good methods were afterwards obliterated by the bad fashion of the searing-iron." [63]

From the side of philosophy as well as physiology, it is interesting to note how the Pneumatic School represents a stage in the mind's search for a vital principle to account for the living man, and more specifically to account for the animal heat, which is a clearly vital quality, and yet indicative of ill whenever it rises above a certain degree, as in fevers, or whenever it falls below, as at the approach of death. From Homer downward, the breath of man suggested itself as the vital principle or its vehicle. How about its relation to the body's heat? This perplexing question brought great confusion.[64] Air seems both hot and cold; and any one can blow hot or cold with the same mouth. Was the vital and necessary breathing of the air, in and out, a cooling or a warming of the body? Opinions wavered and contradicted each other for centuries. Apparently — the whole matter is exceedingly obscure — the early physicists with Hippocrates were ranged on the side of warming, and Aristotle with his great influence on the cooling side. Nearly two thousand years later, Harvey remained perplexed. After his death, the search was carried on more vigorously for some needed and explanatory process analogous to the burning of combustible things, in fine, for a process of combustion. The goal was reached through the discovery of oxygen and the slow-won knowledge of its functions in the human economy.

V. THE FINAL SYSTEM: GALEN

GALEN represents the final catholic and systematic interpretation of Greek medicine and its relation to the sciences of which it was or might make part. He was more than a great eclectic, for his work was a constructive synthesis, with elements added which were the result of his own observations and experiments.

Like other men he was fashioned and driven by his education, into which entered the intellectual past of himself and his contemporaries. But, unlike any other of his time, his genius was so universal that he was impelled and aided throughout his whole career by the entire intellectual past, rather than by one or more of its component interests or typical tendencies.

The sciences which might be related to medicine met in him, with some branches of discipline with which physicians trouble themselves no longer. From his education and still more through his talents and temperament,

[98]

he was a logician and a rhetorician, a master
of speech and composition. He was instructed
in all branches of natural philosophy or science.
A physicist in his ultimate considerations of
the constituents of the human organism as a
part of Nature, he was far more actively a
biologist in his investigation of the same. His
writings show medicine as part of biology.
And indeed his treatment of medicine as the
centre of a larger whole indicates the Greek
unity of science, a unity afterwards to be lost,
but today gradually reviving in the thought of
those who see that the formal barriers between
the sciences are vicious obstructions.

Hippocrates regarded medicine as the healing art. Although in fact he proceeded scientifically, following the method of observation
and induction, and necessarily making use of
working hypotheses, nevertheless as far as
possible he set himself against theory. He
refused to base medical practice upon theories
as to the constitution of the world and man,
and protested against permitting such to divert
the practitioner from the teaching of his experience. The rival school of Cnidus may
have tried to be more scientific, in the sense
of seeking to conform their practice to basic

hypotheses concerning man and his diseases. It was not without its lasting influence; one may perhaps regard Erasistratus as its final great descendant. But, fortunately, the Hippocratic principles triumphed at the time, and appear to have remained dominant during those earlier periods when occupation with theory would have warped and checked the progress of the healing art.

Between the time of Hippocrates and the year 130 A.D., when Galen saw the light, well-nigh six centuries had passed. Long and well-husbanded experience had improved medicine and surgery. The knowledge of the human body had been greatly added to, and the passing theories as to the nature and causes of disease had not seriously obstructed a continuous improvement in the treatment of disease and bodily injuries. Rather, one may think that the rivalry of the different schools, composed of the nominal adherents of different theories, had prevented dogmatism and narrowness in practice.

Galen flourished in the second half of the second century A.D., dying in the year 201. Greek or Greco-Roman faculties of observation were becoming less vigorous and the atmosphere of religion and religious philosophy, which belonged to the dawning of a different era, was already tending to becloud man's vision of the natural world. Further advance in exact science could not be expected, nor was medicine likely to gain much more from the clear and undeflected observation of its practitioners. Its ancient course was well-nigh run.

Magnificently was it to be concluded in the achievements of Galen's genius. He was born at Pergamus in Asia Minor. An intelligent father took care that he received the best education that the town afforded in grammar and rhetoric, as well as mathematics, natural knowledge and philosophy. One may assume that the varied stores of ancient philosophy and knowledge had been rifled by this prodigious learner, when at the age of seventeen he decided to devote himself to medicine. Pergamus afforded good masters and opportunities for practice, especially in its widely sought *Asclepieion,* where patients were treated skillfully, and sometimes cured by miracle. Galen's readiness to recognize miracles was rather significant of the time and ominously prophetic.

Having drained the opportunities of Pergamus, he set out to extend his knowledge at the chief seats of medical learning — at Smyrna, at Corinth, and above all at Alexandria. After nine years he returned a finished physician, already noted for his skill and his authorship of anatomical and physiological treatises. Again he left his native town, this time for Rome, where he won fame and enmity alike, and the patronage of the great. Perhaps his enemies drove him thence, or the plague may have hastened his departure for the east: not an heroic soul was this extraordinary Galen. Emperors called him back, Lucius Verus and Marcus Aurelius; he came, yet would not accompany the latter on his campaign against the Marcomanni, but undertook the care of the young Commodus, at Rome, — not an absorbing business. The last thirty years of his life were devoted to medical research and authorship; — authorship indeed! he had composed some four hundred treatises when he died.

Galen was no condenser! His universal learning, his ready memory, the quick ranging of his mind, his exhaustless powers of argument, his facile rhetoric, conceit of himself, love of belittling others, all piled up the monument of his redundant compositions; yet such was his skill and genius that the monstrous bulk of his writings was not for long to obscure the significance of their contents. After Aristotle, he was perhaps the greatest of the ancient systematizers of natural knowledge. His central endeavor was to make medicine into a systematic science; and, for good or ill, truth and error, he appears to have accomplished it.

Medical practice and physical theory must be made into a consistent unity. To this end Galen sought to base the healing art upon a knowledge of disease and its causes, and to set his pathology upon the anatomy and physiology of the human organism in health. This more fundamental knowledge came through observation under the guidance of philosophy, logic and mathematics. Himself a mathematician, he tried to apply the proofs of Euclid to the results of observation and experiment. He would have the _à priori_ certitudes of the understanding as well as the assurance of experience.[65] But alas! the demands of his philosophy distorted the perceptions of his senses. Moreover, his logic was more untiring than his observation. Yet when he made experiments, as he did frequently, through the vivisection of animals, it was with masterly cleverness.

Unquestionably Galen's over-aptness at finding a purpose and use for every organ, — a use and purpose which made the organ what it was — contributed to his dominance in the centuries after him. Today we are disposed to find his truer greatness in his investigation of the physiology of animals, by vivisection. For example, although the presence of some blood in the arteries had been sensed before him, he would seem to have been the first to demonstrate it. He was a great contributor to experimental physiology, though unfortunately he came at the close of the ancient time, when no man was to follow him to continue his discoveries. Says Dr. Garrison:

" He was the first to describe the cranial nerves and the sympathetic system, made the first experimental sections of the spinal cord, producing hemiplegia; produced aphonia by cutting the recurrent laryngeal; and gave the first valid explanation of the mechanism of respiration. He showed that the arteries contain blood (by performing the Antyllus operation), and demonstrated the motor power of the heart by showing that the blood pulsates between the heart and a ligated artery, but not beyond it. Like the Alexandrians, he inferred that the arteries and veins anastomose through certain invisible and extremely small vessels. He also showed that an excised heart will beat outside the body, a common incident at the sacrificial rites, and good evidence that its beat does not depend upon the nervous system. In these matters Galen gave to medicine that method of putting questions to nature and of arranging things so that nature may answer them, which we call experiments." [66]

In the depths of his mind, Galen was seeking to combine Hippocrates and Aristotle. He drew from the former the fruitful conception of the vital unity of the human organism, vital in its power of living and nourishing itself, and when sick or wounded of regaining its normal state through the *vis medicatrix naturae*, the restoring power of its own nature. The human organism was strictly a unity: the singleness of its life could not be divided. From Hippocrates he took also the four humors, and, as it were, from any source one chooses, the four elements of fire, water, earth and air, and the four primary physical qualities of cold and warm and dry and moist

He drew, nay he drained, his teleology from Aristotle, and, like the Master, applied it to every part of the organic structure: Nature makes nothing without a purpose, and nothing in vain. When Galen is considering the nature and action of an organ, or of the body generally, his mind passes quickly from the sheer description of the thing, and even from the consideration of its efficient cause, and springs forward to grasp its final cause or purpose: therein lies the explanation of the thing, and the explanation, nay the true description, of the function which it is its nature to fulfill. Galen's passionate preoccupation with the purpose of a living organ, colors and even fashions his description both of the organ itself and of the process through which it performs its function.

The function of the body generally is to afford a setting for the soul or life. The bearer of life, or of the vital forces vivifying the body and directing it to the performance of its functions, is the *pneuma*. Entering with the breath, it becomes threefold: the psychic *pneuma* (or, in English, the animal spirits), working in the brain and through the nervous system; the life-*pneuma* (or vital spirits) of the heart and arteries; the physical *pneuma* (natural spirits) dwelling in the liver, and through the veins making blood and nourishing the body and its growth. The liver draws its supplies from the stomach and intestines.

The life of the body fulfills itself in these three functions of the *pneuma*. The various parts — organs and tissues, solids and fluids — are thereby made into a whole, and united in their ultimate function of promoting the individual's life. Health consists in their coöperation in proper proportions according to the age, sex and mode of life of the individual. Sickness is a disturbance of these proportions and of this harmonious working. Between sickness and health lies a condition of predisposition to one or another form of disease, due to the individual's constitution or temperament.

Inception, increase, summit, and recession make the four stages of acute disease. In addition to this rather Hippocratic view, the Galenic treatment proceeded from the principle that every disturbance of function necessarily implied a pathological affection of the parts in question. The physician first decides whether the power of the *physis,* or nature of the body (a Hippocratic conception), was of itself able to cure the part and restore its function. He acts only when nature has proved inadequate. He should consider the inception of the disease, decide upon its causes, and endeavor to remove them or prevent their action. He should resort to further counteracting measures as the pronounced symptoms of the disease declare themselves.

Galen conceived the *physis* as the sum of the powers which impel the body's parts to perform their functions. In the sick body one or the other of these powers exceeds or is deficient in its action. The physician's care must first of all concern itself with the expelling power, which produces the excretions and evacuations of the healthy body, and in sickness expels the matter of the disease. The attracting, restraining and alterative powers are then to be investigated; and the skillful physician will perceive which is defective or too violent, and treat the patient accordingly.

The working principles of Galen are mainly those of Hippocrates. It is in the endeavor to establish them in science and philosophy that Galen goes far beyond the man he called his master. In this endeavor he combined the greater knowledge of the six hundred years' experience with disease which lay between him and Hippocrates, considering and weighing (not dispassionately!) the views of the leading intervening physicians. He was also a brilliant investigator himself, and through his dissections and vivisections advanced the sciences of anatomy and physiology. Even here he erred, not infrequently, through applying the anatomy of pigs and apes to the human body, which he did not dissect. Beyond this he was led, and sometimes astray, by his conviction of the sufficiency of his medical theories and the philosophy of nature on which he sought to base them. He was over-confident in himself and his knowledge, and many a pillar of his medical temple was destined to fall. Yet the great building endured for fifteen centuries.

To describe or sketch the contents of Galen's writings would require a volume. They cover medicine, and, one might say, biology; they concern themselves with philosophy, with psychology, and even with the arts. Many of them were great and valuable treatises, as, for example, that on *The Places* (*or parts*) *Affected*. It sets forth the importance of reaching a clear decision as to the part affected and the nature of the trouble, and proceeds on the principle that there can be no disturbance in the function without an affection of the part. After some chapters of general consideration, the means of making the proper local diagnosis throughout all the parts of the body are considered successively and in detail.

Equally valuable are his treatises on *Therapeutics* and *Hygiene;* and large and important compositions are devoted to the methods of the various medical sects, — Galen was a tremendous medical polemicist. A famous treatise is that of the *Use or Utility,* to wit, the function and purpose, *of the Parts.* Through its long course, with great detail, it seeks to exemplify and prove the Aristotelian principle that Nature makes nothing in vain. It demonstrates that the parts and organs of the body could not be better disposed, and that they are perfectly adapted to the fulfillment of their functions. It discerns and would prove the perfect harmony among the different parts. There are in it constant disquisitions upon final causes, references to God and Nature, and corresponding diatribes against those who accept the action of chance and the theory of the atoms.

The comparatively short but compendious treatise *On the Natural Faculties*,[67] that is to say, the powers inherent in the *physis* or nature of the human individual, reflects many of Galen's characteristics, and may be noticed briefly.

The ancients, Galen for example, were more addicted to personification than ourselves, who have substituted processes for persons, thus using a more commonplace word to express what is still mysterious. The " processes of nature " is a common phrase, while Galen thinks of nature somewhat as an artist, accomplishing her works by τέχνη, which is art. The human *physis* or nature is endowed with its own powers of attraction and repulsion. More broadly and perhaps profoundly speaking, it is alive, possessed of life, which is the sum of its natural powers. Galen is not far from modern vitalistic thinking.[68]

It has been said that there were many Galens; and, indeed, the tract before us exhibits various intellectual processes and methods which we should be surprised to find combined in any one modern person. In it Galen is biologist as well as physician. It evinces penetrating observation, with close reasoning on the data of very clever vivisection. In it Galen also is a philosopher; and offers the reader much *à priori* reasoning and sheer intellectual construction. He is a Greek, in love with logic, with dialectic, with reasoning upon hypotheses. For him, intelligent people are " those who understand the consequences of their hypotheses "; whereas we should be more apt to speak of " those who know what they are talking about."

Galen is under the necessity of finding names and categories for his thinking. Sometimes with him to formulate a statement, devise a concept, give a satisfactory name, is his nearest approach to an explanation, almost equivalent to understanding a phenomenon or process. Much that he says of the three powers of genesis, growth, and nutrition are his verbally satisfying statements of what was, and still is, essentially unknown. Such statements are sops to the insatiate reasoning mind. Galen makes them such as seem to him to " save the phenomena " in each case, and also so that they will dovetail; for he is always a system-builder. Had he known something of chemistry, he would have made his statements such as would " save " other recondite phenomena. His more

detailed arguments sometimes seem but to am-
plify his general or introductory phrases.

It is the work of Nature to form all the parts
of the animal while still in the womb, and
after birth to bring the animal to its full size,
and maintain it. This is a threefold effect, and
the activities are three, "namely genesis,
growth, and nutrition. Genesis, however, is
not a simple activity of Nature, but is compounded of alteration and shaping. That is to
say, in order that bone, nerve, veins, and all
other [tissues] may come into existence, the
underlying substance [69] from which the animal
springs must be altered; and in order that the
substance so altered may acquire its appropriate shape and position, its cavities, out-
growths, attachments and so forth, it has to
undergo a shaping or formative process." [70]

Then, proceeding from the partly false anal-
ogy of the semen and the seed cast into the
earth, he enlarges his descriptive detail, without, of course, penetrating any further into the
process itself. He next takes up the faculty of
growth, which "is one of increase and expansion in length, breadth and thickness of the
solid parts of the animal (those which have
been subjected to the moulding or shaping

process). Nutrition is an addition to these without expansion."

The faculty of growth is present in the embryo, but subordinate to the genetic faculty until birth. Then, till the animal has reached its full size, the faculty of growth dominates while the alterative and nutritive faculties act as its handmaids. " What then, is the property of this faculty of growth? To extend in every direction that which has already come into existence, that is to say, the solid parts of the body, the arteries, veins, nerves, bones, carti-lages, membranes, ligaments, and the various simple and homogeneous coats of the stomach, intestines, arteries, etc."

Galen then describes how children stretch and blow up pigs' bladders; but the bladders get thinner as they are expanded. The children cannot make the bladder get bigger, as only Nature can, through nourishment.

" It will now, therefore, be clear to you that nutrition is a necessity for growing things. For if such bodies were distended, but not at the same time nourished, they would take on a false appearance of growth, but not a true growth. And further, to be distended *in all directions* belongs only to bodies whose growth is directed by Nature; for those which are distended by us undergo this distension in one direction but grow less in the others. . . . Thus Nature alone has the power to expand a body in all directions so that it remains unruptured and preserves completely its previous form."

As for nutrition, the third of these great faculties: " When the matter which flows to each part of the body in the form of nutriment is being worked up into it, this activity is nutrition, and its cause is the nutritive faculty. Of course, the kind of activity here involved is also an alteration, but not like that occurring in the stage of genesis. For in [genesis] something comes into existence which did not exist previously, while in nutrition the inflowing material becomes assimilated to that which has already come into existence. Therefore the former kind of alteration has been termed genesis and the latter assimilation." [71]

Nowadays this description would be supplemented, or superseded, by a description of the multiplication of the body-cells in the growth of tissue, both extra- and intra-uterine, — which we perceive and can to some extent describe, but still cannot account for, save as a power of nature.

In other parts of his tract, Galen argues vigorously against what Erasistratus and others had said — and well said — as to the action of the bodily organs upon mechanical principles and according to the capacities of their forms. Galen's vitalism carries him into many a false counter-argument. His fundamental view may be given mainly in his words:

"Thus every hypothesis of channels [72] as an explanation of natural functioning is perfect nonsense. For if there were not an inborn faculty given by Nature to each one of the organs at the very beginning, then animals could not continue to live even for a few days. . . . For there is not a single animal which could live or endure for the shortest time if, possessing within itself so many different parts, it did not employ faculties which were attractive of what is appropriate, eliminative of what is foreign, and alterative of what is destined for nutrition. On the other hand, if we have these faculties, we no longer need channels, little or big, resting on an unproven hypothesis, for explaining the secretion of urine and bile, and the conception of some favorable situation (in which point alone Erasistratus shows some common sense, since he does regard all the parts of the body as having been well and truly placed and shaped by Nature).

" But let us suppose he remained true to his own statement that Nature is ' artistic,' — this Nature which, at the beginning, well and truly shaped and disposed all the parts of the animal, and, after carrying out this function (for she left nothing undone), brought it forward to the light of the day, endowed with certain faculties necessary for its very existence, and, thereafter, gradually increased it until it reached its due size. If he argued consistently on this principle, I fail to see how he can continue to refer natural functions to the smallness or largeness of canals, or to any other similarly absurd hypothesis. For this Nature which shapes and gradually adds to the parts is most certainly extended throughout their whole substance. Yes, indeed, she shapes and nourishes and increases them through and through, not on the outside only. For Praxiteles and Phidias and all the other statuaries used merely to decorate their material on the outside, in so far as they were able to touch it; but its inner parts they left unembellished, un-wrought, unaffected by art or forethought, since they were unable to penetrate therein and to reach and handle all portions of the material. It is not so, however, with Nature. Every part of a bone she makes bone, every part of the flesh she makes flesh, and so with fat and all the rest; there is no part which she has not touched, elaborated, and embellished. Phidias, on the other hand, could not turn wax into ivory and gold, nor yet gold into wax: for each of these remains as it was at the commencement and becomes a perfect statue simply by being clothed externally in a form and artificial shape. But Nature does not preserve the original character of any kind of matter; if she did so, then all parts of the animal would be blood, — that blood, namely, which flows to the semen from the impregnated female, and which is, so to speak, like the statuary's wax, a single uniform matter, subjected to the artificer. From this there arises no part of the animal which is as red and moist [as blood is], for bone, artery, vein, nerve, cartilage, fat, gland, membrane, and marrow are not blood, though they arise from it."

These passages are from the opening chapters of the second book. The last part of the first book and the remainder of book two present the working of the innate attractive and alterative powers of the organs, whereby they take and transform whatever nutriment is needed for their functions. Galen writes as a physiologist or biologist, though he has in mind the medical usefulness of his matter. The opening paragraph of the third book gives his final summary of this subject:

" It has been made clear in the preceding discussion that nutrition occurs by an alteration or assimilation of that which nourishes to that which receives nourishment, and that there exists in every part of the animal a faculty which in view of its activity we call, in general terms, alterative, or, more specifically, assimilative and nutritive. It was also shown that a sufficient supply of the matter which the part being nourished makes into nutriment for itself, is ensured by virtue of another faculty which naturally attracts its proper juice [humour]; that that juice is proper to each part which is adapted for assimilation, and that the faculty which attracts the juice is called, by reason of its activity, attractive or *epispastic*. It has also been shown that assimilation is preceded by adhesion, and this, again, by presentation, the latter stage being, as one might say, the end or goal of the activity corresponding to the attractive faculty. For the actual bringing up of nutriment from the veins into each of the parts takes place through the activation of the attractive faculty, whilst to have been finally brought up and presented to the part is the actual end for which we desired such an activity; it is attracted in order that it may be presented. After this, considerable time is needed for the nutrition of the animal. Whilst a thing may be even rapidly attracted, on the other hand to become adherent, altered, and entirely assimilated to the part which is being nourished and to become a part of it, cannot take place suddenly, but requires a considerable amount of time. But if the nutritive juice, so presented, does not remain in the part, but withdraws to another one, and keeps flowing away, and constantly changing and shifting its position, neither adhesion nor complete assimilation will take place in any of them. Here too, then, the [animal's] nature has need of some other faculty for ensuring a prolonged stay of the presented juice at the part, and this not a faculty which comes in from somewhere outside but one which is resident in the part which is to be nourished. This faculty, again, in view of its activity our predecessors were obliged to call retentive." [73]

The latter part of the third book is largely devoted to an exposition of the genesis and action of the four humors, which (Galen maintains) Hippocrates, Aristotle and others of the ancients, correctly and sufficiently set forth. He professes no one could " offer anything wiser than what has been said " by them. Yet even here, and still more palpably through other portions of this work, and indeed throughout all his writings, he does not follow Hippocrates and Aristotle as implicitly as he professes. He had learned more than either of them knew of the conduct of the body in health and disease. Yet, had he kept closer to the principles of sage Hippocrates, his writings would have shown a wiser reticence, and more respect for the actual boundaries of the writer's knowledge.

But Galen built his system out of his intellectual inheritance. His treatment of the old materials was affected by the mentality of the second century, in which he shared. He contributed personally the fruits of his own acute observation and experiment, and brought to bear upon the whole his extraordinary power of coördinating disparate elements into a system.

Galen represents the closing development of Greek biology and medicine. The Galenic system was a preservative amalgamation of Aristotle and the Hippocratic tradition with whatever was added by Galen himself. No need to enlarge or change it, since the incapacity of the following time for scientific investigation and even for fruitful clinical observation prevented the further growth of biological or medical knowledge. Dissection and vivisection halted; clinical observation became dulled. Galen marks the end of progress in biology and medicine as his contemporary, Ptolemy, marks the end of progress in astronomy.

Galen's immense influence did not commence in his lifetime, nor arise at once upon his death. Time had to elapse before the sterile centuries felt the need of some unquestionable and encyclopaedic authority on which to base their medicine. As for biology as an investigating science, that had ceased to exist. Among the ancient luminaries in medicine, Galen was nearest to the coming Byzantine and Medieval period not merely in time but in spirit. His systematic treatment of all matters that men need know, his authoritative self-assurance, and above all, perhaps, his completed teleology, or convincing declaration of the purpose of every part and organ of the body, contributed to make of him the source or canon *par excellence* of Arabian and western medieval medicine. In many garbs and forms he reigned for centuries.

VI. THE LINKAGE WITH THE
MODERN TIME

IN WAYS inscrutable as well as in trace-
able currents, Greek biology and medicine
have entered into their greater modern
congeners.   There is no unbroken and continuous record.   Modern biology starts afresh
from observation and experiment, and advances
through   constantly   spreading   avenues   of
scientific research.   Medicine and anatomy
gather impulse from rebellions against the
ancient authorities and rejections of their
statements; Paracelsus (1493–1541), but recently recognized as a great and original physician, declares against the four humors of the
old pathology, asserts that they do not exist,
and publicly burns the works of Galen.
Vesalius, "founder of modern anatomy,"
proves that Galen's anatomical descriptions
are wrong because based on the dissection of
apes and pigs instead of men and women.

Yet even when men think to disavow and
reject, they are affected by what has made part

of their education. For example, after long and baffling vivisections, Harvey demonstrates the systemic circulation of the blood. His discovery has come through years of anxious observation, and not from what he has read (to the contrary!) in books. Yet his reasonings, if not his observations, never free themselves from the influence of Aristotle; and his great discovery sorely perplexes him, since he cannot understand the final cause, that is to say, the purpose, of the blood's rapid round throughout the body: not for generations was this to be cleared up through the discovery of oxygen and the gradual elucidation of the combustion involved in the renewal and cleansing of the system by the blood.

The cessation of growth brings decay to any branch of knowledge. Only further accomplishment can fully utilize and carry on the achievements of the past. Progress alone conserves, coming not to destroy but to fulfill.

Biology was not prosecuted after Galen's time, and the healing arts of medicine and surgery gained little that was new from clinical experience. Vainly they sought to conserve themselves through an eclecticism which tended to become partial and then scholastic. As the faculty of investigation failed, the greater ancient sources were no longer used in the fullness of their contents and living spirit.

In the East, the energies aroused by Islam stemmed the decline of medicine. Among the early " Arabian " physicians (the best of them were Persians) were good practitioners and clinical observers. There was enough active intelligence to demand and support the use of the best sources of medical science, which were of course the Greek. One of these good physicians, the princely Persian, Avicenna (980–1037), was an acquisitive and systematizing genius of the first order. His great " Canon of the healing art," drawn chiefly from Galen and Aristotle, presents the contents of Greek medicine as a closed and serried system. This book was of enormous influence upon medieval Europe, and is said still to rule in the Moslem world.

Nevertheless in Avicenna's " Canon " and in the treatises current in medieval Europe, Greek medicine was embalmed, rather than alive and quick in its creative spirit of investigation. Moreover, medieval physicians and compilers tended to select and use what was on the level of their own appreciation or understanding. So they left untouched much that was best in the Greek medical legacy.

At a later time, say in the sixteenth century, the spirit of scientific observation was stirring more actively, and the epoch-making people of the age worked somewhat in the old Greek way, making ready a period of palpable scientific progress. Such men were fitted to receive the best that the great and ancient past contained, which it now seemed to offer these brighter minds as with a new disclosure.

But in respect to medicine and anatomy there were obstacles to any such acceptance. The men given to actual observation were impatient of the past's authority; they chose to see for themselves. Vesalius was not like those who in his own and prior generations could see in the actual human body what Mundinus or Galen said was there. He was looking for himself, and was vehemently moved at the discrepancy between Galen and the human fact. For him, Galen had ceased to reign.

Thus from the times of Paracelsus, Vesalius and Paré, and then of Harvey, two general factors tended to end the reign of the once dominant Galen. The one was the active scientific spirit — quite like the Greek — impelling these men and their successors to go to nature for their facts, and not accept them from authority; and the other was the concomitant or resulting increase of knowledge of the human body in health and disease, and of other living organisms, as well as of the action of natural agencies affecting them.

Some of these men were even tempted to depreciate the ancients, drawing a breath of relief after the long incumbency, the dead weight, of their authority. Yet as medicine through the seventeenth and eighteenth centuries, and to our own day, continued on its chequered and romantic career, ever and anon there came to it the impulse to take refuge in the old Hippocratic wisdom.

The struggle, nay, the romance of medicine, springs from the desire of the intellectual creature to find a reason, an underlying explanation, to " save " and account for observed phenomena. The thoughtful doctor seeks to account for the action of disease, and find an accordant theory, as well as means of cure. His desire to understand disease keeps him from being satisfied with such remedies as mere experience has shown to be followed with good results.

What man who desires to account for things as obscure as disease, or to accomplish so difficult a task as its cure, can avoid framing a working hypothesis in his mind? He may come to admire and rely on his hypothesis till it grows into a comprehensive explanation, a compelling theory, of life and disease. Any rational means of cure, transcending the groping of haphazard empiricism, must conform to this theory. His working hypothesis was, to be sure, suggested by some facts of observation. But from their child it may become their master. In that case it will be apt to deflect observation, and may cause the observer to see only facts that accord with it.

In pure or abstract science a good hypothesis or theory should account for the facts observed; and new facts may undo it. Till those new facts appear, there may be no call to reconsider the theory, or use it practically. But medicine, on the other hand, is essentially a practice, a healing art. Its function is to cure the sick.

The general appearance and conduct of living beings suggests some conception of life and some idea of the disturbance called disease. This idea may carry a notion of the means of cure, adjusted to the symptoms. The test of validity comes when doctors apply their theories to their patients. If the doctors be intelligent and rationally observant, like the Greeks, clinical, and perhaps too frequently death-bed experience may lead them in time to reject some particular theory of disease and cure. But experience, having overthrown one theory, is likely to lead the doctors to shape another. Thus goes on the alternate conflict and alliance between theory and practice, which makes the intellectual romance of medicine. The character and vicissitudes of this romance are affected from century to century, by the intellectual temper of the time, constructive, for example, or sceptical or eclectic.

This conflict is set forth in that inaugural Hippocratic writing entitled, *The Ancient Medicine*, which argues that the practitioner should have nothing to do with philosophers' theories regarding the universe of things and the nature of man. These theories incidentally find the causes of disease in excessive heat or cold, moisture or dryness. The practice of medicine needs no such vain and superfluous hypotheses. It is a healing *art* learned through the rational teaching of cumulative observation. This ordered store of clinical experience will tell the practitioner when no application of the " hot or cold " theory, but a regulated diet, will benefit the patient.

Yet the Hippocratics used working hypotheses of general application. They conceived them as the fruits of medical experience. The two most famous were the hypothesis of the four humors and that of the *vis medicatrix naturae*, the healing energy of nature herself. The first has been discarded; but the second is in some form and manner still accepted universally in medicine and surgery.

Another fundamental Hippocratic conviction or hypothesis was that diseases came from natural, not demonic, causes, and should be treated by natural remedies rather than by magic. It was this conviction that enabled Greek medicine to become a rational art and possible science. One sees at once its broad affiliation. The assumption of the constant action of natural causes underlies every mechanical art and all physical science. In medicine, the hypothesis that disease is due to natural causes, and should be treated by corresponding remedies, has had a chequered career! Yet one will scarcely beg the question in saying that it has been accepted by the best medical practice from the time of Hippocrates to our own day!

One might write an interesting history of medicine, as the story of the conflicts and alliances between theory and practice. One should, however, bear in mind that the differences among the doctors of any period in the actual treatment of disease have been less marked than their controversies might seem to indicate.

Celsus told us of the Empirics who protested that they would have nothing to do with remote and hidden causes; of the Methodists who were partial to generalizations. More interesting were the Pneumatics, with their vital principle of the *Pneuma*, an idea almost as old as man. Yet these ancient schools were not so very wide apart in practice.

A century later, Galen, sagaciously surveying the medicine of his own time and the older teachings, strove to make a system from his conceptions of the medical wisdom of Hippocrates and the biology of Aristotle. Although a great observer, he was in love with logical *à priori* construction: with him, intelligent people were " those who understand the consequences of their hypotheses."

[132]

From Galen we leap forward to his would-be overthrower, Paracelsus, who cast off the old theories, yet reached back his hand to Hippocrates as a wise practitioner and profound observer of the courses of disease, like Paracelsus himself! His younger contemporary, Vesalius, investigating with his own hands and eyes, rejected much of the old anatomy, and apparently troubled himself little with medical theory. But Harvey — to mention only one feature of the working of this great intelligence — was harassed by the craving to reconcile the circulation of the blood with the Aristotelian physiology or teleology of the natural parts of man. And if Harvey's discovery of the systemic circulation appears as the fruit of investigation and experiment, his pregnant contribution to the theory, or knowledge, of generation was in itself an hypothesis (acceptable no longer!), to wit: *omne vivum ex ovo.*

Practice and theory! medicine must have both; and when clinical experience has taught its lessons, the microscope and laboratory become the chief means of medical advance. The wise practitioner, though he turn his mind from theorizing, will still be he who proceeds upon some sane working hypothesis.

Belonging to Harvey's own generation, the extraordinary Fleming, van Helmont, forms a link between Paracelsus and the theorizing systems of the medico-chemical and medico-physical schools of the early seventeenth century. The chemical school (Sylvius of Leyden may be called the founder) starts from the conception of *fermentation* through the action, for example, of the saliva and gastric juices upon foods. Health consisted in the proper balance of acids and alkalies, and sickness in the excess of one or the other. The cure lay in the reduction of the excessive element. On the other hand, the physicists, starting from the admitted circulation of the blood, sought a physical or mechanical interpretation of all bodily processes. Health lay in their unimpeded action.

Since the physical as well as chemical knowledge of that time was utterly inadequate for the basis of sound medical practice, a reaction was to be expected. The advocates of these theories had drawn more than one conception from Greek medicine, to weave into their systems. Now the reaction inaugurated by the Englishman, Thomas Sydenham (1624–1689), directed itself toward the conscious acceptance of the principles of Hippocratic practice. Not improperly was Sydenham called " the English Hippocrates." Although conversant with the natural sciences of his time, he refused to base the practice of medicine upon any theory drawn from them, even as Hippocrates and his school had refused to base their medicine upon the theories of the Greek physical philosophers.

Like Hippocrates, Sydenham set himself in every case to study the whole course of the patient's disease, observing the succession of symptoms, and the response of the patient to the treatment employed. Like Hippocrates, he conceived a disease as the struggle of the body's healing energy — the *vis medicatrix naturae* — with the noxious agent. He divided the symptoms into: (1) those essentially pertaining to the action of the noxious cause; (2) those arising from the reaction of the patient's system; and (3) those induced by the treatment. He developed the conception of successive phases of disease, and of the pernicious or benignant symptoms pertaining to them.

Sydenham, again like Hippocrates, concerned himself chiefly with acute disease. A malady became chronic through the slowness

[135]

of the patient's reaction or the persistence of the noxious agent. And, finally, he showed himself true to the Hippocratic spirit in refusing blind obedience to any authority (even that of Hippocrates himself, whose reputed works he had studied diligently) and in testing everything by observation. His spirit is reflected in a passage from one of his letters referring to his own medical writings:

" I have been very careful to write nothing but what was the product of faithful observation, and neither suffered myself to be deceived by idle speculations, nor have deceived others by obtruding anything upon them but downright matter of fact." [74]

With Sydenham and the turn toward Hippocratic methods, we may leave this romance of the conflict and alliance between medical theory, or medical science, and medical practice. To continue it exceeds my space as it does my powers. We have the word of the veteran of medical science and medical history that Hippocrates and Sydenham " did useful work for mankind in the twilight." Sir Clifford Allbutt has loved them well, these great forbears of his, kin to each other though two thousand years apart. But now Sir Clifford, speaking in 1919, deems that a new birth of medicine is taking place: " What is then the new birth, this revolution in medicine? It is nothing less than its enlargement from an art of observation and empiricism to an applied science founded upon research; from a craft of tradition and sagacity to an applied science of analysis and law; from a descriptive code of surface phenomena to the discovery of deeper affinities; from a set of rules and axioms of quality to measurements of quantity." *Sursum corda!* — Lift up your hearts! Before us spreads a fair prospect of the reconcilement of theory and practice, in a final system of scientific medicine!

However this may be, we have recently realized, as never before, the vast range and complexity of the elements entering our mentalities; and we who may live to witness the new revolution, should also be ready to recognize the indirect, the obscure yet basic, influence of Greek medicine. The modern medical man no longer looks to Galen or Hippocrates for specific instruction; but he well may make his own the spirit of the Hippocratic writings and the wise principles of Hippocratic practice. He may still take to himself many a Hippocratic precept; and well for him and all with whom he came in contact if he have drawn into his nature, and reflect in his professional conduct, the Hippocratic ethics of the healing art.

And if modern medicine and biology no longer draw directly from the old Greek store, we still may reflect upon the antecedent influence by which we profit. The guiding knowledge, which we no longer need, did its work in our immediate or mediate predecessors, and thus led on to us. The shoulders that *we* stand on are the taller because the men before us, or the men before them, stood upon the shoulders of the Greeks. So the Greek foundation stones have their place in our edifice of knowledge. And still at the summit waves the flag of *nature,* — the old Hippocratic φύσις — as the healer of the body's ills: νούσων φύσεις ίητροί, *vis medicatrix naturae.* Today more universally than ever, if not more profoundly, we realize that the power of an organism to heal or restore itself is one of the universal marks dividing all living organisms — plants, and animals, and man — from the inorganic world.

BRIEF OUTLINE OF INFLUENCE OF GREEK BIOLOGY AND MEDICINE

Christian Fathers, including St. Augustine, (354–430) — Teleological view of the human body.

Abstractions from Galen:

Oribasius (325–423),

Paulus of Aegina (625–690),

Alexander of Tralles (525–605), zealous Galenists.

Hippocrates and Galen, in Arabic (almost slavish devotion):

Rhazes, (c. 850–c. 923), in theory a Galenist, in practice, Hippocratic;

Avicenna (980–1037); the " Canon," based on Galen;

Avenzoar (Hispano-Arabic, c. 1072–1162), disciple of Galen;

Averroës (1126–1198), through whom Aristotelian science became known in Europe during the Middle Ages; shook some doctrines of Galen.

Translations of Hippocrates and Galen, from Arabic into Latin: e.g.

Constantine (monk at Monte Cassino) †1087,

Gerard of Cremona, †1185,

Mark of Toledo, c. 1200.

No translation of Aristotle's *Historia Animalium,* or of the *De Generatione Animalium,* of Hippocrates' *De Generatione,* or of Theophrastus' *De Plantis* reached the earlier Middle Age; knowledge of these works might have led to a rediscovery of Nature, centuries earlier, and would have altered the intellectual history of Europe.

Learned revival of 13th century: translations, from the Arabic, but also from the Greek, of texts of Hippo-

crates and Galen who became integral parts in the
medical instruction in Universities for centuries;

Michael the Scot (1175?–1234?); two versions of
Aristotle's *Historia Animalium;*

Albertus Magnus (1206–80), Commentary on *Historia
Animalium;* Albertus began first-hand plant-study
in modern times.

14th century: Nicholas of Reggio translated the treatise
of Galen *On the uses of the* (bodily) *parts,* from
Greek into Latin; the best account of the human
body then available and the starting point of modern
scientific medicine;

Conrad von Megenberg (1309–1398); *Book of Nature,*
founded on Latin versions of Aristotle and Galen.

15th century: Recovery of more Hippocratic and Galenic
texts, which were turned into Latin; e.g., Thomas
Linacre (c. 1460–1524); " De Naturalibus Faculta-
tibus ", 1523;

Isolated Edition of Galen, 1490, but Hippocratic works
first printed in 1525.

16th century: A new biological science, largely due to
Aristotle and Galen, although Paracelsus (1493–1541)
destroyed the ' humoral pathology ', and publicly
burned the works of Galen;

First Greek text of the *Aphorisms* of Hippocrates, 1532,
edited by Rabelais;

Vesalius (1514–1564) the modern " Father of Anatomy ";
though he based his work on Galen, yet he shook
the authority of Galen, by proving errors of Galen;

Antonio Benivieni (†1502) revived Hippocratic tradition by publishing notes of cases, with records of
deaths and post-mortem examinations, — as did
Amatus Lusitanus (1511–c. 1562), of Portugal;

Ambroise Paré (1517–1590), "Father of Modern
Surgery "; though no classical scholar, profoundly
influenced by classical traditions;

Fabricius ab Acquapendente (1537–1619), founder of
modern embryology and an Aristotelian;

William Harvey (1578–1657), founder of modern experimental physiology, the greatest biologist since Aristotle, whose work *On Generation* is a commentary on Aristotle in the Aristotelian spirit of return to nature.

17th century: Great revival of Hippocratic tradition:
  Thomas Sydenham (1624–1689) " The English Hippocrates ",
  Herman Boerhaave (1668–1738).

18th century: Partial eclipse of the ancients, through scientists' absorption in direct investigation of Nature; cf., e.g.,
  C. Linnaeus (1707–1778),
  Georges Cuvier (1769–1832).

Rediscovery of the significance of Hippocrates and of the Aristotelian biology, — a modern achievement:
  R. T. H. Laënnec (1781–1826), inventor of stethoscope; valuable hints derived from Hippocratic writings;
  Francis Adams (1796–1861); praise of Hippocratic surgical treatises;
  Johannes Müller (1801–1858),
  George H. Lewes (1817–1878),
  William Ogle (1827–1912);
  all derived direct inspiration from Aristotle's biological works, in spite of independent research work.

NOTES AND BIBLIOGRAPHY

NOTES AND BIBLIOGRAPHY

1. Cf. John Burnet, *Early Greek Philosophy*, London, 1920, [3] p. 70.

2. "From quotations I had seen I had a high notion of Aristotle's merits, but I had not the most remote notion what a wonderful man he was. Linnaeus and Cuvier have been my two gods, though in very different ways, but they were mere schoolboys to old Aristotle," in Letter of Darwin to Ogle, 1882, cited by Arthur Platt, in the preface to his translation of the *De Gen. Animalium;* also by Charles Singer, "Biology," p. 200, in R. W. Livingstone's *The Legacy of Greece,* Oxford, 1921.

3. W. A. Heidel, " Περὶ Φύσεως, a study of the conception of Nature among the Pre-Socratics," in *Proceedings of the American Academy of Arts and Sciences,* XLV. 105 (1910).

4. W. A. Heidel, o.c., p. 106. Professor Heidel has rendered service to scholarship in bringing forward the interpretative value of the Hippocratic writings. In saying "Hippocrates," Professor Heidel is not intending to decide the specific authorship of the tracts drawn upon.

5. I refer to the Περὶ Διαίτης, *On Diet,* and the Περὶ Γονῆς, *On Generation.* A sketch of their contents is given by Charles Singer, in Livingstone's *The Legacy of Greece,* Oxford, 1921, pp. 168 ff.

6. The great edition is that of Littré in ten volumes, with almost too ample introductions, and containing the Greek text printed opposite the French translation. Émile Littré, *Oeuvres Complètes d'Hippocrate,* Paris, 1839–53. While Littré was bringing out his volumes, in the middle of the nineteenth century, a good English translation, with judicious introduction and notes, was made of *The Genuine Works of Hippocrates,* by Francis Adams, under the

Auspices of the Sydenham Society, London, 1849, and New York, 1886. These writings vary in wisdom and knowledge, and not all of them seem to emanate from the same school. Hippocrates was of an Asclepiad family, and born on the island of Cos, where a temple school of medicine already flourished. He is the supreme representative of the Coan school. The doctrines of the rival school of Cnidus were disapproved by him, yet will be found to have crept into some of the writings included in the Hippocratic *Corpus*.

The Cnidian school was a little earlier than the Coan, and admirable in its practice. Unfortunately for us, and for its own repute, the Cnidian writings are lost. Plato's irony has ruined the Sophists, and the slurs of the Church Fathers on such of their opponents as the Gnostics cannot be repelled by men whom time has rendered voiceless. We wish that the Cnidians also could speak for themselves.

7. The short piece Περὶ Τέχνη — *Concerning* [the] *Art* [of healing], in the sixth volume of Littré's edition, argues that there is a real medicine or healing art, which, for example (§ 11), enables the physician to infer from other symptoms what is not visible to the eye in internal disease.

8. Heidel's translation, o.c.

9. The writer of the tract has not in mind those working hypotheses or pre-suppositions, which every man of science uses in systematic observation and experiment; he is thinking of the hypotheses which would ascribe all disease to an excess of warmth or cold, dryness or moisture; for this does not tally with common experience.

10. Water, unmixed with wine, was not highly thought of in ancient Greece.

11. *On Ancient Medicine,* § 13, Adams' translation, o.c., slightly modified.

12. Heidel's translation, o.c. (a very little changed).

13. Adams' Translation, o.c.

14. The attention of Hippocrates and his school was fastened upon acute diseases; chronic affections were regarded as a result of them.

15. Adams' Translation, o.c.

16. Says Charles Singer, after citing some of these

Aphorisms: " No less remarkable is the following saying: ' In jaundice it is a grave matter if the liver becomes indurated.' Jaundice is a common and comparatively trivial symptom following or accompanying a large variety of diseases. In and by itself it is of little importance and almost always disappears spontaneously. There is a small group of pathological conditions, however, in which this is not the case. The commonest and most important of these are the fatal affections of cirrhosis and cancer of the liver, in which that organ may be felt to be enlarged and hardened. If therefore the liver can be so felt in a case of jaundice, it is, as the Aphorism says, of gravest import," in *The Legacy of Greece,* o.c., p. 232.

17. Largely Adams' Translation, o.c.

18. Adams' Translation, o.c.

19. A common Hippocratic operation was opening the patient's chest to relieve the accumulation of pus in cases of *empyema,* following pneumonia. Cf. Charles Singer, in *The Legacy of Greece,* o.c., p. 228.

One may note that the names of these two diseases and, for that matter, a considerable part of medical nomenclature are from Hippocrates.

20. In *The Legacy of Greece,* o.c., p. 236.

21. This is apparent when he is seeking to orient himself in his subject, as in the opening chapters of the *De Partibus Animalium.*

22. Assuredly Leonardo, if ever mortal man, is entitled to be called a universal genius; and his dissections of human bodies and animals were joined in his mind with mathematics and mechanics, though not with philosophy. But unhappily Leonardo's marvellous anatomical drawings remained unknown and exerted no influence upon other investigators, so far as may be ascertained. See H. Hopstock, " Leonardo as Anatomist," in Charles Singer's *Studies in the History and Method of Science,* Oxford, 1921; II. 151–191.

23. D'Arcy Wentworth Thompson, *Historia Animalium,* English Translation, Oxford, 1910; William Ogle, *De Partibus Animalium,* English Translation, Oxford, 1911;

Arthur Platt, *De Generatione Animalium*, English Translation, Oxford, 1910.

24. Sir Arthur Hort, *Theophrastus' Enquiry Into Plants, with an English Translation*, in *The Loeb Classical Library*. 2 vols. New York, 1916.

25. Aristotle refers to the vivisection of a chameleon in *Hist. An.*, II. 11. (503 b.)

26. See Charles Singer, "Greek Biology and its Relation to the Rise of Modern Biology," in Singer's *Studies in the History and Method of Science*, Oxford, 1921; II. 1–100.

27. It is more elaborately discussed in *De Partibus Animalium*, II. 1 ff. (646 a.)

28. *De Gen. An.*, II. 1. (731 b.)

29. *De Partibus Animalium*, I. 5. (645 a.); says Henri Poincaré: "We seek reality, but what is reality? The physiologists tell us that organisms are formed of cells; the chemists add that cells themselves are formed of atoms. Does this mean that these atoms or these cells constitute reality, or rather the sole reality? The way in which these cells are arranged, and from which results the unity of the individual, is not it also a reality much more interesting than that of the isolated elements . . . ?" Again: ". . . it is in the relations alone that objectivity must be sought; it would be vain to seek it in beings considered as isolated from one another." *Foundations of Science*, (1913), p. 217 and p. 350.

30. *De Partibus Animalium*, I. 1. (641 b.)

31. *Hist An.*, VIII. 1. (588 b.–589 a.)

32. Περὶ Φύσιος παιδίον, *On the Nature of the Embryo*, § 29, cited by Singer, o.c.

33. *Hist. An.*, VI. 3. (561 a.)

34. D'Arcy W. Thompson, *On Aristotle as a Biologist*, (Herbert Spencer Lecture, 1913), Oxford, 1913. Cf. also, in greater detail, Charles Singer, in his "Greek Biology," etc., o.c., pp. 29 ff., which contains other examples of Aristotle's penetrating observation aided by dissection.

35. Cf. William Ogle, *De Partibus Animalium*, English Translation, Oxford, 1911; Int., p. 27.

36. Charles Singer, "Greek Biology," etc., o.c., pp. 19, 20.

[148]

37. A like need impelled Immanuel Kant to conceive a metaphysical scheme, suited to his apprehension of the natural universe.

38. *De Gen. An.*, I. 1. (715 a.)

39. This passage unconsciously suggests that possibly the motor or even the final cause lay implicit in the reasonings of the old philosophers. Elsewhere Aristotle says: " The ancient Nature-Philosophers . . . did not see that the causes were numerous, but only saw the material and efficient, and did not distinguish even these, while they made no inquiry at all into the formal and final causes." *De Gen. An.*, V. 1. (778 b.)

40. All of these passages are from *De Partibus Animalium*, I. 1. (640 b. ff.)

41. *De Gen. An.*, I. 1. (715 b.)

42. The " heterogeneous " parts; see *Ante.* It is Bichat's (1771–1802) distinction between tissues and organs.

43. *De Partibus Animalium*, II. 11. (646 b.)

44. *De Partibus Animalium*, IV. 10. (687 a.)

45. *De Gen. An.*, V. 1. (778 a.) and the notes of the translator.

46. *De Gen. An.*, II. 3. (736 a.) and see the translator's note to the passage.

47. This very attractive generalization is not to be pressed too far.

48. *Hist. An.*, VIII. 1. (588 a.)

49. *De Gen. An.*, I. 18. Darwin held to a theory of pangenesis, but it is not commonly accepted.

50. *Hist. An.*, VIII. 2. (589 b.)

51. *Hist. An.*, VIII. 12. (596 b.)

52. Collected in E. H. F. Meyer's *Geschichte der Botanik*, Königsberg, 1854–57; I. 88 ff.

53. Sir Arthur Hort, see n. 24.

54. Of which Meyer, o.c., gives a synopsis, I. pp. 167 ff.

55. Julius von Sachs, *History of Botany*, 1530–1860, Translation by H. E. F. Garnsey, Oxford. 1890; examples, pp. 17, 42, 376, 450.

56. *Enquiry*, I. 1. 9.

57. *Ibid.*, I. 1. 4. The last clause in the last sentence is

not translated thus by Hort. Singer's rendering seemed to me more probable, — though I have made a slight modification at the end. For it seemed to me less question-begging to translate τῶν μελλόντων as "what they are about to be," rather than "what they are becoming," as Singer does.

58. *Ibid.*, I. 1. 11.

59. *Ibid.*, III. 8. 1; Cf. II. 6. 6. Sometimes what the ancients took for "male" and "female" were really different species.

60. *Ibid.*, II. 8. 4.

61. Charles Singer, "Greek Biology and its Relation to the Rise of Modern Biology," in Singer's *Studies in the History and Method of Science*, Oxford, 1921; Vol. II. p. 98.

62. For the next few pages I have followed, in the main: Theodor Meyer-Steineg, *Geschichte der Medizin*, Jena, 1921; Max Neuburger, *History of Medicine*, Translation by Ernest Playfair, Oxford, 1910; Vol. I.; Sir T. Clifford Allbutt, *Greek Medicine in Rome*, London, 1921.

63. Soporific or some kind of *anesthetic expedients* seem to have been used commonly, to deaden pain.

64. Sir Clifford Allbutt does not eliminate this confusion, properly enough, from his interesting discussion of the matter, in chapter X of his *Greek Medicine in Rome*, o.c.

65. Cf. III. 1. with III. 2. of Galen; *On the Natural Faculties, with an English Translation* by Arthur John Brock, in *The Loeb Classical Library*, New York, 1916.

66. F. H. Garrison, *Introduction to the History of Medicine*, Philadelphia, 1921,[3] p. 105.

67. Galen, *On the Natural Faculties*, o.c., n. 65.

68. Brock, in his *Introduction*, p. XXX, compares him with Bergson.

69. Why not protoplasmic?

70. *On the Natural Faculties*, Brock's *Translation*, o.c., I. 5.

71. *On The Natural Faculties*, Brock's *Translation*, o.c., I. 5–8, with an occasional verbal alteration.

72. I. e. ducts, etc., the morphological factors empha-
sized by Erasistratus.

73. Brock's *Translation*.

74. Quoted in the Article on *Sydenham*, in the *Dic-
tionary of National Biography*. I have, in these last pages,
chiefly followed Meyer-Steineg and Sudhoff, *Geschichte
der Medizin im Überblick mit Abbildungen*, Jena, 1921.

Our Debt to Greece and Rome

AUTHORS AND TITLES

AUTHORS AND TITLES

AESCHYLUS AND SOPHOCLES. *J. T. Sheppard.*

GREEK RELIGION. *Walter Woodburn Hyde.*

SURVIVALS OF ROMAN RELIGION. *Gordon J. Laing.*

MYTHOLOGY. *Jane Ellen Harrison.*

ANCIENT BELIEFS IN THE IMMORTALITY OF THE SOUL. *Clifford H. Moore.*

STAGE ANTIQUITIES. *James Turney Allen.*

PLAUTUS AND TERENCE. *Gilbert Norwood.*

ROMAN POLITICS. *Frank Frost Abbott.*

PSYCHOLOGY, ANCIENT AND MODERN. *G. S. Brett.*

ANCIENT AND MODERN ROME. *Rodolfo Lanciani.*

WARFARE BY LAND AND SEA. *Eugene S. McCartney.*

THE GREEK FATHERS. *James Marshall Campbell.*

GREEK BIOLOGY AND MEDICINE. *Henry Osborn Taylor.*

MATHEMATICS. *David Eugene Smith.*

LOVE OF NATURE AMONG THE GREEKS AND ROMANS. *H. R. Fairclough.*

ANCIENT WRITING AND ITS INFLUENCE. *B. L. Ullman.*

GREEK ART. *Arthur Fairbanks.*

ARCHITECTURE. *Alfred M. Brooks.*

ENGINEERING. *Alexander P. Gest.*

MODERN TRAITS IN OLD GREEK LIFE. *Charles Burton Gulick.*

ROMAN PRIVATE LIFE. *Walton Brooks McDaniel.*

GREEK AND ROMAN FOLKLORE. *William Reginald Halliday.*

ANCIENT EDUCATION. *J. F. Dobson.*